LOOKING

AT MY

HEART

LOOKING

STEIN AND DAY/*Publishers*/New York

AT MY
HEART

BY DR. PHILIP BLAIBERG

With acknowledgment to Benjamin Bennett, well-known South African author, for his valuable assistance and cooperation in the preparation of the manuscript for this book.

DEDICATED
to my late son
ISRAEL HARRIS

ACKNOWLEDGMENTS

The author wishes to express his sincere thanks to:

The leader of the Transplant Team, Professor C. N. Barnard, Associate Professor and Head of the Cardiac Thoracic Unit, for the wonderful job he did on me;

Professor V. E. Schrire, Associate Professor and Head of C.S.I.R., Cardiac Vascular Pulmonary Research Unit;

Dr. W. Beck, Senior Cardiologist;

Dr. S. C. W. Bosman, Registrar;

Dr. J. F. Hitchcock, Registrar;

Dr. C. Venter, Registrar;

Mr. R. P. Hewitson, Senior Surgeon;

Mr. T. G. O'Donovan, Senior Surgeon;

Dr. M. S. Barnard, Surgeon;

Dr. J. Ozinsky, Senior Anesthetist;

Dr. M. C. Botha, Immunologist;

Dr. G. M. Potgieter, Chemical Pathologist;

Dr. E. Simson, Pathologist;

Dr. R. Mibashon, Haematologist;

Professor L. Eales, Physician;

Professor A. Kipps, Virologist;

Dr. G. N. Thatcher, Physician;

Professor P. E. S. Palmer, Radiologist;

Professor R. E. Parks, Radiologist;

Dr. Jane Chambers, Physician;

Dr. S. Bank, Physician;

Dr. A. A. Forder, Bacteriologist;

Dr. B. Nel, Superintendent of Out-Patients Department and Tranplant Unit;

Miss M. Sternweiler and Miss S. Strydom, Physiotherapists;

Mr. L. W. Piller, Senior Cardiac Technician;

Miss S. Joseph, Assistant Cardiac Technician;

The Sisters and Nurses of the different day and night shifts;

Mr. Johann van Heerden and Mr. Alistair Hope, Heart-Lung-Machine Technicians;

The Hospital Dietitian, Mrs. H. J. B. Stevens, and staff;

Staffs of the various laboratories;

Mr. Ishmail Abdol, the laboratory cleaner, responsible for the sterilization of bedpans, mops, and urinals.

Then last, but not least, Mrs. Dorothy Haupt, who without hesitation gave her consent to have her late husband's heart transferred to me. I salute you, Mrs. Haupt, and will be grateful to you forever.

Should I inadvertently have omitted anyone who should have been included in this illustrious list of names, I can only say that it was done unintentionally, and I apologize.

CONTENTS

FOREWORD by Cyril Adler   11

1   Beginnings   15

2   A Fateful Puncture   33

3   Should A Doctor Tell?   48

4   Enter Doctor Barnard   65

5   Operation Transplant   84

6   Sealed Off   103

7   Life with a New Heart   147

EPILOGUE: Back from the Brink, BY Benjamin Bennett   181

FOREWORD

How fortunate and privileged we were to have witnessed a great moment in the history of medicine when Professor Christiaan Barnard and his team at Groote Schuur Hospital, Cape Town, successfully transplanted a human heart! This moving and dramatic surgical achievement was, in the second instance, carried out on my friend the writer of this book, Dr. Philip B. Blaiberg, who submitted himself to the operation knowing full well the risks which were involved.

When Dr. Blaiberg asked me to write a foreword to his book I accepted eagerly, for it gave me the opportunity to pay a personal tribute to a man who by his courage, fortitude, and faith contributed in no small measure to the successful outcome of an epoch-making operation.

Little did we guess in the year 1928 when Dr. Blaiberg lived with us in Johannesburg when he was a first year dental student at the University of the Witwatersrand, that he would be fated to obtain a new lease on life through the progress of medicine and the surgical skill of a team of doctors. If I may be permitted to speak for all his friends, we congratulate him on the successful outcome of his ordeal and hope that the courage and spirit he displayed will serve as an example to all who suffer ill health.

My friendship with Philip goes back some forty years and despite the fact that he spent several years in England completing his dental course, was on full time active service as a Dental Surgeon in the Middle East and Italy during World War II, and subsequently established himself in Cape Town, our families have always been in close touch.

With increasing illness during the past few years, he found it necessary to dispose of his private practice, and, knowing my interest in historical medicine, he decided to donate to the Museum of the History of Medicine in Johannesburg a foot operated drill which he had used some years previously. The gift of this drill, historic in its own right and associated as it is with Dr. Blaiberg, brings him very near to those of us at the Museum and it is of intense interest to visitors as having belonged to the man who was one of the central figures in this great epic.

The history of medicine throughout the ages records the exciting events and the names of those who have played a part in the development of medical knowledge and skills, and to this list of great names there must surely now be added that of Dr. Philip Blaiberg.

I salute and pay a heartfelt tribute to my loyal friend for his extraordinary bravery and indomitable will and wish him and his family an increasingly healthy future.

Cyril Adler, M.B., B.Ch., D.Phys. Med.
Honorary Director,
Museum of the History of Medicine,
Johannesburg, *May 1968.*

1

BEGINNINGS

Only a few months ago I lay in the hospital, a dying man with a stricken heart. It had deteriorated until it scarcely beat. I gasped for breath. I could barely lift a hand or foot. The nurses wondered how soon my bed would be ready for the next patient.

Then came the miracle: I was given a new heart, a new lease on life.

Today I am the second man since the Creation to live with the heart of a dead man beating in his breast, able to declare that a heart is not the seat of the emotions, of love and hate, good and evil, greed and generosity; to prove it is a pump that can wear out or be damaged and, like a car part, replaced to continue the task of powering the engine of the body.

At this moment there are millions of other heart sufferers the world over, their lives despaired of, waiting as I did for death, often welcoming it as a merciful end to their own long-drawn-out agony and the helpless distress of their loved ones.

Perhaps what has happened *to* me and what medical science has done *for* me and others since will bring hope to many now on the verge of death. For the future holds possibilities of heart banks stocked for transplants, the renewal of impaired and failing valves, and the chance of prolonged life where none existed before.

This is my story.

My father, Jacob Woolf Blaiberg, was born in 1870 in the Polish town of Crajevo just inside the present Polish border. He had his early education in Prussia, in the town of Lück, where he stayed with his grandfather.

Like other Polish youths at the time he was called up for military service in the army of the Czar, Poland then being under Russian rule. This was bitterly resented, an imposition to be avoided at all costs, and many conscripts escaped with the assistance of smugglers who, for a fee, helped draftees escape across the border into Germany.

My father was one of those who arranged to be spirited away while marching to the station on the way to a troop camp. No serious effort was made to trace or capture him for the reason that the N.C.O. in charge of the draftees was himself in the plot.

From Germany my father made his way to England where members of his family were engaged in the furniture trade. For twelve years he worked, and might have married and settled down, like thousands of other Jewish refugees from Eastern Europe, but for the upheaval caused by the Boer War.

He was infected with the prevailing fever to emigrate to South Africa. Other relatives in Salt Lake City, urged him to make his home in the United States, the "land of opportunity," instead of in the "wilds" of Africa. But for him the lure of South Africa was greater. He had heard of its gold and diamonds, of quick fortunes to be made, its warm sunshine and wonderful climate, so different from London's cold and choking fogs, the adventurous life that awaited young men there.

He invested his hard earned savings in family-made furniture and shipped it to Cape Town. It was a shrewd move. English furniture, like many other commodities in short supply in South Africa after the war, was eagerly sought; and he found a ready and profitable market for his goods at the Cape.

He traveled the thousand miles by train to Johannesburg with £600 in his pocket, a considerable sum in the early 1900's. The much vaunted "City of Gold" was, however, a great disappointment to him. He saw no gold, and the wood and iron structures, dirty streets, and coarse mining town atmosphere depressed him. He asked himself whether he had, after all, made a wise decision and come to the right place.

When he was relieved by some light-fingered gentry of two well-cut and highly prized, London-made coats, his mind was made up. Without regret or delay he left Johannesburg and its opportunities—he could probably have invested his £600 in land worth millions today—and returned to the Cape to look for a business that would bring him a decent living in more honest and salubrious surroundings.

He was offered, and bought, a tiny country store at Uniondale Road, a railroad station about fifty miles from Oudtshoorn, a town in the Eastern Cape on the route from Cape Town to Port Elizabeth. The main advantage of the store was that it stood just outside the boundary fence of the station and the owner was assured of the custom of the railwaymen who lived with their families in the vicinity, the farmers in the district, and passengers who left the trains to stretch their legs and stroll into the shop, which offered a wide variety of household goods, clothing, foodstuffs, and sweets.

With the store my father inherited a general factotum named Charlie, who, apart from his cook-and-bottle washing activities, also served behind the counter. This contributed, in due course, to the business getting in the red, though it must be added that my father, freed from

17

the monotony of the upholstery trade, also spent a good deal of his time playing cards with the railwaymen and police personnel, living off the shelves, and sharing a barrel of brandy ordered monthly from a neighboring farm.

That was before he met my mother.

She was, in many respects, a remarkable woman. Not only was she hard-working and shrewd but had a vigorous personality, with the will and determination to get what she wanted. In days when women were expected to leave the running of affairs to the menfolk and look after their large families at home, she was bold and assertive, with complete faith in her judgment.

Named Gertrude Leah Portnoi, she was born in a small Lithuanian town in 1890. She lost her father when she was in her early teens, and her mother was left with a son and four daughters to support.

The son, Isaac, was, like my father, conscripted into military service. But he made no effort to evade it. He had a natural aptitude as a horseman and marksman and, within a short time, rose to the rank of sharpshooter.

On his discharge he sailed for South Africa and embarked in business as a speculator in the Eastern Province. He had a gay and easygoing disposition, which soon made him a favorite with the farmers, but what they most admired in him was his unerring marksmanship. He could do anything with a rifle that a Boer could do and often very much better.

After a lapse of time and infrequent letters that eventually ceased altogether, my uncle's mother became anxious about his welfare and safety. Africa to her was a primitive land where lions and other wild beasts stalked, like the wolves in Russia, and it was decided after much anxious discussion that one of her daughters should go to

South Africa and find out what had happened to Isaac. My mother, the second eldest daughter but the most self-reliant, was chosen for the journey.

She was only eighteen and knew no languages but Lithuanian and Yiddish, but fortunately a letter announcing her impending arrival reached Isaac ahead of her. He met her at the dock in Port Elizabeth and took her to a farm in the nearby Uitenhage district where he had arranged for her to stay. She quickly adapted herself to farm life and learned to speak Afrikaans fluently. She soon discovered and reported back to her mother that Isaac was a fairly successful businessman who liked and enjoyed the good things of life but, in her opinion, was far too extravagant. Used to the hard life of the average Jewish family in Lithuania, she saw no sense or benefit in living beyond one's means as her brother did. She herself saved all she could.

The agricultural show at Port Elizabeth in those days was an important event in the lives of the townsfolk and farmers alike. The farmers would arrive in their wagons and carts to exhibit their prize stock and produce and discuss over the coffee cups politics, the drought, and prices. Their wives, clad in their Sunday best, would often accompany them to savor a little of town life away from their daily chores.

It happened, by coincidence, that my father as well as Isaac and Gertrude Portnoi attended the show of 1907. Isaac had visited Uniondale Road in the course of his travels and had a nodding acquaintance with my father. He introduced him to his sister.

Then aged thirty-seven, tired of a bachelor existence and yearning for a Jewish life in a Jewish home, my father saw in Gertrude Portnoi a desirable young woman with whom he could settle down. He proposed and was

19

accepted. Isaac gave them his blessing, and they were married in a synagogue. Soon afterward Isaac resumed his travels, this time to the United States, where he settled in Pittsburgh. His family heard no more of him.

My mother arrived at Uniondale Road to find her new home a flat-roofed, wood-and-iron structure, or shanty, with what were euphemistically called "living quarters" adjoining. They consisted of three poky rooms with a few sticks of furniture and a kitchen. The "bathroom" was an old galvanized iron tub that was set in the kitchen on bath nights and filled with water boiled in paraffin tins on a wood-burning stove. In winter the rooms were perishingly cold and in summer, a furnace.

My mother made no complaint. It was a wife's duty to help her husband, not grouse or grumble. She reconciled herself to the spartan existence, but her acceptance of the living quarters did not blind her to the fact that all was not well with the business. She soon realized that her husband was too easygoing and lackadaisical to make a success of it. If it was to survive, she would have to take control at the earliest opportunity.

This decision was precipitated by the arrival of a grim-faced man from Port Elizabeth who informed her that he had been sent by a firm of merchants to take stock prior to making my father insolvent. My mother pleaded with him for time. Explaining that she had only recently arrived at Uniondale Road and was not responsible for the management, or mismanagement, of the business or Charlie, she assured him that all debts would be paid within three months. The man was impressed by her earnestness and sincerity, as well as by her business sense, and gave her the period of grace she asked.

At the end of three months all outstanding accounts had been paid and the business saved. But now my mother laid down *her* conditions. She insisted that Charlie had to go, that the card-playing cease forthwith, and the monthly order of the barrel of brandy be canceled. Henceforth it was she who approved accounts and supervised the store. My father's duties were to keep the books and handle correspondence.

She also presented the railway and police personnel with an ultimatum: unless they returned to their offices and duties, instead of wasting their time in the Blaiberg store, she would report them to their superiors. This immediately had the desired effect.

An exception was the brandy which arrived, as usual, at the end of the month. My mother promptly put an axe through the barrel and spilt the precious contents on the ground. My father made no objection. In fact, he became a fanatical teetotaler who carried his convictions to such lengths that he refused to drink a toast in liquor at my own wedding.

My mother worked fifteen hours a day, from dawn until after the last train had passed through the station at nine o'clock at night. Those were the days before dining cars. She obtained the contract to sell coffee, cakes, and sweetmeats to passengers who alighted during the scheduled stops at Uniondale Road and soon had the reputation of serving the best Java coffee, with rich creamy milk, along the line. It also netted the business a profit of £40 a month.

Her enterprise did not stop there. She tendered for, and was awarded, the contract to carry the Royal Mail from Uniondale Road to the little town of Uniondale, fifteen miles distant, and back. The mail was conveyed in a Cape cart drawn by four horses and driven by an old Malay who heralded his arrival, and departure, with blasts on a battered old bugle. There was also accom-

21

modation in the cart for three passengers who endured considerable discomfort while bumping over pot-holed roads but contributed to the Blaiberg till.

My mother was a strictly orthodox Jewess, observing all the dietary laws and the hygiene of the kosher kitchen: she even made use of the Royal Mail cart to transport specially killed kosher meat from Uniondale. However, she opened the store as usual on the Sabbath. She accepted cash for articles bought but refused to write or cut dress materials. The customers had to use the scissors themselves. With her retentive memory, she was able to tell my father, on Saturday nights, the names of customers who had bought on credit during the day and the amounts they were to be charged.

In later years I used to argue with her about her qualified observance of the Sabbath. I maintained that as she opened the store for business on the Sabbath, she might as well break the other prohibitions as well. Otherwise, it was sheer hypocrisy. She did not agree. In her view, it was not possible "for practical reasons" to close the store on the Sabbath. One had to make a living and provide for one's family, but Sabbatical injunctions should be observed wherever possible. We never agreed on the point.

I was my parents' first-born. I was brought into the world on May 24, 1909 by an old Scottish doctor at the home of Jewish friends in Uniondale. Up to the age of six, when I was sent to the local farm school, my playground was the store and railway station, my playmates the children of the stationmaster and of my parents' helpers in our house and store. The delight of my life was to watch the trains steam in and out and listen to the fairy stories my father told me as he prized open the cases of merchandise that arrived from Cape Town and Port Elizabeth.

22

Our farm school had only one teacher, Miss Maria Terblanche, who taught fifteen or sixteen children all subjects in the curriculum from kindergarten to Standard Six. They included the three R's and the song "The Blue Bells of Scotland," whose words were Greek to me though I loved the tune. I spoke only Afrikaans then. I knew no English until I was nine years of age though my parents spoke English and Yiddish between themselves when they discussed their private affairs.

At about this time my mother decided that she had lived in a shanty long enough, and our improved finances warranted the building of a new shop of brick with a pitched roof, together with living quarters, stables, and outside rooms for railway passengers to sleep overnight.

Life continued in the new shop and living quarters as before, though we were far more comfortable. Travelers brought news from the outside world, there was convivial conversation and discussion, and tea was served, free of charge, at night in the feeble glow of a solitary paraffin lamp.

When I passed into Standard One at the farm school, I had acquired a vocabulary from the railway workers that would have made a Billingsgate fish porter look to his laurels, if not blush. This, coupled with the fact that my mother believed the time had arrived for me to have a Jewish and Hebrew education, induced her to send me to the nearby town of Oudtshoorn where I boarded with a private Jewish family and was assured of strictly kosher meals.

I attended the Government School which was unique in that a period was devoted each day to Hebrew tuition. At first I felt thoroughly miserable and longed for Uniondale Road, my pals, the trains, and the stories my father told me. However, after a week I was included, on trial, in a rugby team and was soon nicknamed "Fly-berg" because of the way I used to bullock my way for the goal line, regardless of the tackles and tacklers I encountered on the way. I was speedy, tough, and strong, much more robust than the average townboy.

I was at school at Oudtshoorn when World War One ended. I remember still the celebrations on Armistice Night, November 11, 1918, with fireworks exploding in the sky, car horns blaring, and the townsfolk singing joyfully to mark the end of the war to end all wars.

Conditions at Uniondale Road changed with the times. Cars became commonplace. Cooperatives were formed, and farmers no longer depended so much on the country store for buying their requisites and selling their produce. My parents' once thriving business dwindled, and they moved to Oudtshoorn; the store at Uniondale Road passed into the hands of relatives.

While still at school in Oudtshoorn I toyed with the idea of becoming a pharmacist, working white-coated in the fascinating world of test tubes, chemicals, and drugs that doctors prescribed for their patients' ailments. I had passed the Junior Certificate examination, begun my two-year matriculation course, and bought my text books when suddenly I felt I was wasting my time. I wanted to embark on my life's career at a local pharmacy without delay. My friends might not have an idea what they intended to do when they left school but I did—*now*.

I told my father of my ambition. He did not hesitate. "By all means," he said, "*if* you have really made up your mind. Pharmacy is a good profession. But are you sure this isn't a passing fancy?" I told him I had never been more certain of anything in my life.

He arranged to have me indentured—in those days possession of a Junior Certificate qualification was sufficient—and I set out blithely for work with a condescending smile at my friends on their way to school.

Disillusionment came soon. Instead of being invited into the dispensary and introduced to its secrets, I was told to sort out baby food posters stacked beneath a tiny stairway. They were needed, I was told, for a window display the following day when a special effort would be made to stimulate the sale of baby foods to young mothers. I toiled all day amid the dust and cobwebs and emerged dirty and sweaty with a bundle of the precious posters. It was not my idea of pharmaceutical training or endeavor. An uneducated messenger could have coped with the task equally well.

"Well," my father asked me at table that night, "how did you like it?" I was noncommittal. Pride prevented me from confessing my role in the projected baby food sales campaign on the morrow.

My second day was more or less a repetition of the first, though now I was permitted to speak to customers. To one I sold two razor blades for the price of one. For another I could not find a preparation that was staring me in the face. My employer treated me to a homily on knowing the stock, where it was kept, and not giving the public something for nothing, even if it were only a razor blade.

My father must have noticed I was downcast that night. To his further questions about my day's activities, I replied miserably, "Dad, I would like to go back to school."

For the first time he raised his voice to me in anger. "Go back to school? All right! But, remember, you can't go through life chopping and changing. When you decide on something, as you did, and say you are sure about it, you've got to go through with it.

"And don't ask me," he added, "to tell your employer that you intend to leave. That, you'll have to do yourself."

Next day when the doors closed at 1 p.m. as usual on Wednesdays, I approached my employer. In fear and trembling and with thumping heart, I confessed I was not happy, that pharmacy was not exactly what I had expected, I wanted to become a schoolboy once more.

He looked at me sternly. "If you want to leave," he said, "you can. I won't miss you. But, in the future, see to it that you don't waste people's time like you have mine." I said nothing about the time I had wasted recovering his baby food posters.

Back at school, amid much banter, I had to repurchase my books, rejoin the matriculation class and catch up as best I could. I was never allowed to forget my unhappy experience. Our chemistry master, one of the old-fashioned English types who invariably taught with his mortar board, rarely asked a question of the class for the next two years without prefacing it with, "Wait a moment. Let's ask Blaiberg, the chemist. He'll know!"

I matriculated at the Oudtshoorn Boys' High School in 1927 and enrolled at the University of the Witwatersrand in Johannesburg in 1928. Since my pharmacy days, my leanings had been toward engineering, but I believed, perhaps wrongly, that engineering required a first-class, or exceptional, mathematical brain, which I did not possess. So the dental profession gained another recruit; it was the year the Dental Faculty at the university produced its first crop of finalists.

After a year I sailed for England and enrolled at the Royal Dental Hospital, London, where I remained for four years. I did well at my studies and was regarded by one of my instructors, Mr. Maurice Allmen who taught me to make my first dentures, as one of his "brighter" students, "always inspired by new ideas."

He also found me, according to his reminiscences in a Brighton, England, newspaper recently, "full of bravado and fond of a joke," and he adds that I was forever trying to make him drunk! I cannot remember how I got, or came to deserve, that reputation which apparently still abides with one who is now verger of St. Bartholomew's Church in Brighton. But I will accept another of his recollections that I was always willing to take a chance. I believe in taking chances. They have usually come off.

I was happy at the hospital, and I loved London. I played a good deal of rugby, trained hard, and was tough as nails. It was good to be young and strong and alive with never a day's illness. At the end of the most strenuous game, I had plenty of wind and was ready and eager for an evening's entertainment and gallivanting.

I had the honor to be chosen captain of the 1931-1932 team when the Royal Dental Hospital reached the first round in the inter-hospital cup competition for the first time in twelve years. In one game I made a high tackle, grabbing my opponent around the head. My hand somehow got into his mouth. My opponent shook me off but not before a press photographer caught me. The caption to the photograph was derisive. "Good dental work!" it proclaimed.

On another occasion I got a beautiful black eye while playing against London Hospital. My assailant, though I am sure he meant no harm, was none other than George Stevenson, who was later appointed Surgeon-Commander in the Royal Navy.

In the summer seasons I played cricket not, I must confess, because I enjoyed or had any particular ability but in order to participate in country fixtures that were

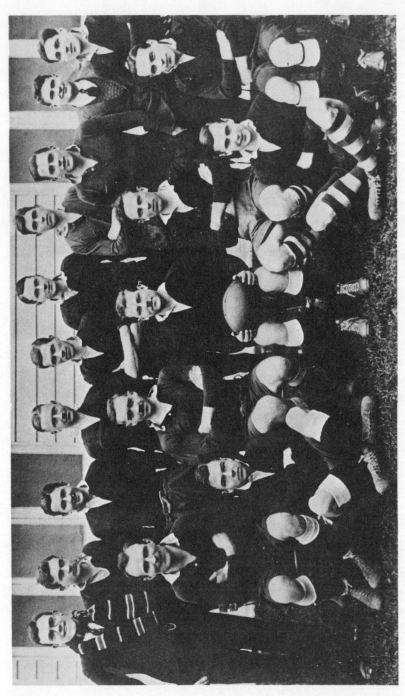

Dr. Blaiberg, Captain (with ball, front row) of the Royal Dental Hospital Rugby Team, 1931-1932 season.

Good dental work—Philip Blaiberg's
tackle is a little too high.

marked by good *al fresco* lunches and barrels of delicious English beer.

I spent my annual holidays on the Continent, roughing it in cheap hotels, sitting up at night in third-class railway coaches and eating sparingly at inexpensive buffets. No millionaire tourist enjoyed himself more. I sailed the Rhine from Mainz to Cologne, admired the medieval castles and the Lorelei, and did all the other things young, carefree students do on vacation.

I graduated in June, 1933, to the great delight and pride of my parents, and sailed for Cape Town a full-fledged dental surgeon.

2

A FATEFUL PUNCTURE

Romance can begin at any time and in any circumstances. Mine began with a puncture. I was driving home with my mother to Oudtshoorn when the steering wheel wobbled. I got out of the car in the bitter cold of a winter night to see, as I feared, a punctured tire.

Unable to find a lever to remove the wheel and replace it with the spare, I realized I would have to start a fifteen mile trek to a garage in Oudtshoorn with scant hope of meeting a car or getting assistance on the way. Leaving my mother, though not without some anxiety, I set out, pondering gloomily my ill luck on my homecoming. I had walked about a mile when, to my relief, a car came into view. I hailed the driver, who was accompanied by a man and a girl. When they learned of my plight, they agreed to take me back to my car.

There, the driver picked up my crank handle and, pityingly, showed me that one end was fashioned for removing a wheel. I had not driven a car for four years in England and was unaware of this new development in car tools. The wheel was soon changed, and off I drove to Oudtshoorn to a family welcome and celebration.

"What a blithering idiot," one of the girl's companions said. The idiot was, by this time, well out of earshot.

Several nights later at the Oudtshoorn cinema I noticed

an attractive blonde with blue eyes and trim figure. She smiled vivaciously at me at interval. Things should not be so bad, I told myself, with such talent around. I spoke to her after the show. She then told me she knew me— she was in the car when her companions helped me change my wheel, and she had also been at school with me though I had been in a higher class. Her name was Eileen Abel, daughter of Israel Harris Abel, Oudtshoorn hotel proprietor, and she worked as shorthand-typist-bookkeeper.

She did not add, then, that I was the only youth of seventeen she had not invited to her "batmitzvah" (confirmation) party on her thirteenth birthday before I left for London; she had regarded me as serious beyond my years, the equivalent these days of a square. Mabel Lewin (now Mabella Ott-Penetto, a well-known opera star in Europe) and one of her friends who lived in Oudtshoorn at the time were of the same opinion. They dubbed me "papa." I had, however, not been unduly perturbed or offended by the lack of an invitation to the party. I preferred sports to girls in those days.

Soon after my return, I started practice in Robertson, a town in the Cape Province, about 150 miles from Oudtshoorn. I returned home several months later to spend the Jewish Day of Atonement with my family. On the eve of the twenty-four-hour fast, I looked up from my seat on the ground floor of the synagogue and saw Eileen Abel, directly opposite, in the women's gallery. We eyed each other throughout the service, paying little attention to our prayers or the tuneful chanting of the cantor. A spinster who watched us—though her eyes, too, should have been concentrated on her prayer book—inquired of Eileen later when she could wish her *mazeltov* on her engagement.

34

I walked Eileen home that night. I realized I was in love. So did she.

I will leave it to Eileen to tell you the story of our romance and courtship. After thirty-two years of married life, there are events that have faded or vanished from my memory. Not so with Eileen. Womanlike, she can tell many a story of me in those far-off days, of lovers' quarrels always quickly made up and how much we were in love.

"From that night in the synagogue," she says, "our romance blossomed. I lived from one long weekend to the next. We wrote love letters and telephoned each other regularly. But between his visits I was terribly lonely. In those days the car journey between Robertson and Oudtshoorn was long and dreary, with shocking roads and two steep mountain passes. We both felt so far from each other.

"The highlight of our courtship of two years, which to a young girl seemed much longer, was our first holiday together at a pleasant little seaside resort, Mossel Bay, about sixty miles from Oudtshoorn. In those days young people were more aware of the conventions than they are now. We booked at different hotels so that it would appear we met by chance instead of by arrangement.

"We had never been together before for as long as ten days; and well do I remember our swims in the sea, the hikes, picnics, and dancing at hotels by night to the popular tune of the time 'Smoke Gets In Your Eyes.' We danced to it, looking into each other's eyes. Perhaps that is why we were voted, by holiday-makers, the most romantic couple of the season. They could see we were so much in love. Whenever I hear that tune today, it reminds me still of those happy, halcyon days at Mossel Bay.

"Although we both accepted that we would eventually marry, we never discussed a definite wedding date. Phil was building up a practice at Robertson and not earning sufficient to support a wife. Sometimes my parents wondered whether our courtship would ever end.

"I reassured them. 'Don't worry. We must have patience. One of these days Phil will be on his feet, and he'll be able to afford to marry.'

"As the months and years passed I began to wonder, like my parents, whether Phil would ever give me an engagement ring and announce our impending marriage. Then, in August 1935, my father died suddenly while on a trip to Czechoslovakia. Not long afterward Phil came to Oudtshoorn to sympathize with our family. He told me he had a big surprise for me. I demanded to know what it was. He wouldn't tell me. All in good time, he said.

"That night he drove me to a quiet spot outside the town. It was full moon and as bright as day. Putting his hand in his pocket he drew out a number of diamond rings that flashed in the moonlight.

" 'Take your choice,' he grinned. I chose a beautiful solitaire and put it on.

" 'It's lovely, Phil,' I cried. 'It's the most marvelous gift I've ever had. Oh, you've made me so happy!'

"We kissed and lay in each other's arms talking of the future, the happiness we would know together, of all the wonderful things lovers speak of at such precious and unforgettable moments in their lives.

"We got home in the early hours of the morning. I woke up my mother, sisters, and brother to tell them the wonderful news. There was no need to announce the engagement. Next day the entire community of Oudtshoorn knew of it and turned up to congratulate us. Telegrams began to stream in.

" 'Mazeltov,' one read. 'So you're going to marry the blithering idiot after all.'

" 'The idiot' and I had the distinction of seeing our wedding photograph in the intaglio [gravure] section of the *Cape Times*. We were described as among 'The Couples of the Year.' Photographs of country weddings rarely appeared in the city newspapers in South Africa in those days. What a send-off that was on our honeymoon. . . ."

Eileen and I were married in the Oudtshoorn Synagogue on April 5, 1936. I could not have made a better choice. She has been a loving and wonderful wife to me, sharing our joys and happiness, comforting me in time of sorrow and adversity, masking with a smile her anguish when she was told, in confidence, to steel herself for my imminent death.

After our marriage we occupied the best room in the Commercial Hotel for about eighteen months. I found the adage that two can live more cheaply than one perfectly true. My bill, with cardplaying, as a bachelor had amounted to twice our dual account. One of the main reasons for this was that I could no longer dally in the pub before and after dinner as had been my custom. We eventually rented a newly-built house for £6 a month and lived in comfort, if not luxury, on £30 a month.

In 1938 our first and only son, named after his grandfather, Israel Harris, was born. Our cup of happiness overflowed. Holding him on my knees, while he tugged at my tie, was sheer heaven. When we noticed that he was rather slow in beginning to talk, Eileen took him to a pediatric friend of ours in Cape Town. He assured her, after a series of tests, that Harris was a child of well above average intelligence, and he predicted a career for him that would be outstanding. His prognosis was correct.

Besides excelling in everything he undertook, whether sports, scouting or other activities, Harris won the coveted Lindsay Smithers scholarship which enabled him to attend the University of Cape Town for four years to study for an engineering degree. He was awarded a grant for his brilliant record in mathematics and the sciences. His initial year was crowned with first classes in pure and applied mathematics and physics. In his second he received another, augmented, grant. There seemed no doubt he was set for a brilliant career, and we, his parents, were happy and proud.

But, alas, in 1961 we were dealt a shattering blow. Harris died tragically at the age of twenty-three. Our grief was immeasurable. The joy and light seemed to have gone out of our lives. Night after night we sat silently at home.

But Eileen, whose sorrow was no less than mine, faced up to fate's harsh blow and sustained and lent strength to me as she has done throughout my illnesses and the anxiety of the heart transplant operation. She has shown herself a true daughter of Israel and a virtuous wife as exemplified in our Scriptures.

We had one comfort in our days of trial, our daughter Jill, who had been born on September 14, 1947. Eileen, who is passionately fond of flowers, had almost lost her through a threatened miscarriage brought on by over-exertion in our garden. Nothing could replace Harris, but the love, devotion, and understanding Jill showed us somehow helped to fill the void.

My six years in practice at Robertson passed more or

Dr. and Mrs. Blaiberg on their wedding day at
Oudtshoorn, Cape, South Africa, April 5, 1936.

less uneventfully. I made a comfortable living and many good friends. Shortly before the outbreak of World War II we decided to move to Cape Town where I started to practice in the suburb of Woodstock, but it was not to be for long. In 1940 I enlisted as a dental officer in the South African Medical Corps and spent three years in different military camps. It was a monotonous life in many ways, far from the battlefront.

In 1943 I went North with the South African Sixth Armoured Division as second-in-command of the Dental Section. From there I was transferred to a mobile dental unit consisting of myself, a sergeant mechanic, corporal, dental orderly, and an Italian batman. This unit served the railway construction engineers and tunnelling companies.

We increased our personnel with a little fox terrier we found in a bombed-out Italian village. I named him "Molar." He was with us for two years. All the dogs I have since owned have borne his name; the last died at the ripe age of sixteen.

We were in Italy at the time of the German retreat when Kesselring blew up bridges and sections of railway tunnels that our engineers had to repair for trains to be brought up and restore communications. We were assured our engineers would not be able to get traffic moving in less than two years, but they did not know of the two tunnelling companies recruited from the gold mines of the Witwatersrand. Their motto was "Today's record is to-morrow's standard." They worked the clock round in shifts, and trains were running through the tunnels of the Apennines within six months.

I was no hero and did nothing heroic in the war. I did my job behind the lines and had time to philosophize on my chances of survival when ack-ack opened up on the

German bombers threatening to drop their loads in our area.

My attitude has always been fatalistic. What will be, will be. Nothing can be undone. There is, I believe, a destiny that governs people's lives. Many of my fellow servicemen, who survived bombing raids and incredible exploits during the war, were killed in avoidable accidents while sight-seeing in jeeps. I myself escaped death on a number of occasions and feel it was pre-ordained that I be spared for an operation that was to influence the course of medical history.

My first brush with death was when I was a child in kindergarten at Uniondale Road. We had to cross what was usually a dry water bed to reach school. My friend Steffie and I were allowed to go home early one day and played on the way in the sand and shallow pools of water. We were in no hurry. Suddenly I looked up and saw a man racing along the river bank in our direction, waving his arms frantically.

At first I paid little attention. Then I noticed that only twenty-five yards away the river was surging toward us, brown and muddy, the result of heavy rains behind the mountains.

"Look, Steffie," I shouted. We ran for the bank and scrambled up. As we reached safety a vast column of water swept by, carrying boulders and uprooted trees with it. Had we delayed another minute we would undoubtedly have been caught in the flood and drowned. For the next three days, not even a cart and horses could cross the swollen river. The children who left school after us had to stay with farmers until the waters subsided.

On another occasion I strung a hessian rope across the roof of a galvanized iron outhouse adjoining our store.

One end I tied to a wheelbarrow, and the other I used in order to clamber up the straight wall on to the roof from where I shouted to my friends and surveyed the activities on the station.

I did this several times until I happened to notice that the rope had caught on the sharp protruding edge of the roof and was worn through to the last strand. Had it snapped while I was scaling the wall. I would certainly have been severely injured or broken my neck.

Steffie and I were also involved in another adventure which might have had fatal consequences. Playing at the station one day, we decided to take a joyride on an unattended railroader's handcar. We undid the brake and set off gaily down the incline, unaware that a freight train was at that moment approaching Uniondale Road and would have collided with us, head-on, within a short while. Fortunately, a railwayman spotted us as we careened along and set off in pursuit on a bicycle along the tracks.

The handcar slowed down at an ascending incline where our pursuer overtook us. He explained, in explosive language, that we two so-and-so's were heading for disaster. The three of us strove, with might and main, to push the handcar back to the station. We succeeded in clearing the line just in time. I did not resent the belting I got for that escapade. I sometimes wonder what would have happened if the freight train had been a few minutes ahead of schedule.

At about this time I used to take the horses from our stables to water at the river. As I was riding one bareback on our return, he took fright and bolted at breakneck speed for the stables. I had the presence of mind to duck as he entered or I would have been decapitated.

To complete the story of what might be called my

charmed life, there was the occasion when I was in a transit camp and suffered my annual attack of tonsilitis. I was sent to the military section of the Johannesburg General Hospital for a tonsilectomy. Both surgeon and anesthetist were reluctant to operate on a colleague. Something, they said, was "bound to happen." It did!

I collapsed during the operation and turned blue, and they had an anxious time trying to resuscitate me. At last they succeeded. But that was not all. I continued to hemorrhage for hours to the dismay and anxiety of the anesthetist. He was obliged to anesthetise me once more to enable the surgeon to insert a stitch to arrest the hemorrhage. They were glad to see me off the table alive.

At last the war was over and I flew back to South Africa. I looked forward to resuming life with Eileen and my son and enjoying the fruits of peace. But after demobilization came a period of disillusionment. I had hoped to continue practice in Cape Town, but I could find no suitable premises for a dental office. Building had been at a standstill, and all offices were occupied. Extortionate amounts in key money were demanded for tiny rooms in which it would have been difficult to swing a cat.

Former patients had drifted to young men who, without ties or responsibilities, should have been in the forces. It embittered me not a little when I realized how they had feathered their nests while I, and thousands like me, had been away. However, I had the consolation of knowing I had done my duty as I saw it.

Eventually I settled down to practice once more, and patients began to arrive. My leisure hours, especially at the weekend, I spent swimming in the icy waters at Graaffs ("Men Only") Pool on the Atlantic seaboard, sun-bathing, chatting pleasantly with other regulars, hiking along the beautiful paths of Table Mountain, and scaling Lion's Head and Devil's Peak which tower above the Cape Peninsula.

My health between the ages of thirty-six and forty-five, was perfect. I felt fit and full of the joys of life. My practice was improving and the future seemed assured. We bought a six-room, two-story gabled house in Weltevreden Avenue, Rondebosch, one of Cape Town's loveliest southern suburbs. A tall oak tree in the center of a spacious lawn gave shade from the hot summer sun.

To Eileen's disappointment, however, nothing would grow under, or near, the oak until she had the idea of planting pink and blue hydrangeas in its shade. After a few years they grew so tall and flourished so beautifully that they became our pride and a showpiece of the avenue. We were the envy of our neighbors. We were happy in ourselves and in our children.

Then *IT* happened.

3

SHOULD A DOCTOR TELL

One Saturday afternoon in 1955, accompanied by my son, I was beginning the ascent of Lion's Head when I felt a sharp pain in the chest. It was, I told myself, most probably an attack of indigestion but uncomfortable enough for me to abandon the climb and return home. The pain passed.

I called my family doctor, Dr. Wilfred Kohn, who examined me, found nothing wrong but suggested I lay in a supply of glycerine trinitrite tablets, which are prescribed for anginal pains. In the event of another attack, he said, I should take them and report to him.

Exactly two weeks later, Eileen and I were invited out to dinner. We spent a pleasant evening and returned home at about midnight. I lay in bed, reading the weekend newspaper, when I was suddenly racked with severe pains in the chest and arms and began to retch violently. Perspiration poured down my face. From my own medical knowledge, I knew the symptoms were those of a coronary attack.

"Eileen," I gasped, "I've had a heart attack. Quick, call the doctor."

He arrived followed by a specialist who took an electrocardiogram. Both agreed with my diagnosis. I had, indeed, suffered a coronary thrombosis, but they assured me it was nothing serious, not even when I had another, similar, attack a few hours later.

Eileen was, however, told the truth. Out of my hearing, they said the attack was a very severe posterior coronary and that she should steel herself for the "worst," which might happen at any time. In the interests of my health it would be best to make light of the incident.

For the next one and a half months Eileen had to live with a smile on her lips but with fear in her heart, unable to confide in anyone, while I spent three weeks in bed and another similar period resting. Eventually I returned to my office for a few hours a day at first and then on full time.

The illusion, or impression, given me that I had been in no real danger of my life fortified me, especially as my heart condition was so atypical that I suffered no further anginal or chest pains and had no occasion to use the tablets prescribed for me.

My mother had died in her sleep of a heart attack at the age of sixty, but my father lived to the ripe age of seventy-three and there was longevity in his family. In view of my previous record of good health, I had no reason then to believe that I had inherited a heart condition from my mother or that my younger brother, Sammy, who died in Israel in 1966, was similarly afflicted.

Still I thought it prudent to place myself under the care of Professor Velva Shrire, a leading Cape Town cardiologist, who now enjoys an international reputation in his field. As Director of the Cardiac Clinic at Groote Schuur Hospital, he has been called the "brains behind the transplant team."

His career has been marked by outstanding achievements ever since he passed his Junior Certificate examination with five distinctions and a grant in 1931. He matriculated two years later, first in South Africa at the

Kimberley Boys' High School, with five distinctions and three grants. Initially taking a B.S. degree, with honors, in three Majors (anatomy, physiology, and pharmacology), he was awarded his Master of Science in 1938 and in 1940, a doctorate in physiology. After taking his Ph.D. he wrote for his M.B.Ch.B. the following year. He was the Dux of the University of Cape Town Medical School and graduated with ten gold medals.

In 1949 he was awarded the Nuffield Travelling Fellowship in London, became senior registrar at the National Heart Hospital, London, and spent three months in the United States. While in London he was made a Member of the Royal College of Physicians (London and Edinburgh) and returned to South Africa to establish the Cardiac Clinic at Groote Schuur. His fame as a cardiologist and author of medical papers and textbooks has since spread throughout the world with fellowships and honors heaped on him in endless profusion.

Still, he is modest, unassuming, and shuns publicity. Some describe him as taciturn and unapproachable. As a patient I found him kind and sympathetic. My welfare, like that of all his other patients, was always of first importance to him. By selecting me as the second heart transplant patient, he was eventually to save my life.

When he examined me after my first attack, he was apparently satisfied with my condition. My case was filed and he told me I would be advised annually to call on him for routine examination. If, however, anything untoward happened, I was to communicate with him immediately.

I was now put on anticoagulants and instructed to report, every other month, at the prothrombin department of the Cardiac Clinic for a blood test to control the dosage. I was restricted to a fat-free diet and limited to two eggs a week. My family, to keep me company, switched to skimmed milk, ostensibly for weight-reducing purposes; but, for me, the fat-free diet was in conformity with the theory that fat produces cholesterol which, in turn, blocks the blood vessels and precipitates heart disease.

All this raises the old question: "Should a doctor tell the truth?"

Generally speaking, I believe it is right not to tell a patient the truth about his condition, especially if it is grave, for the reason that he might develop neuroses and these, coupled with overanxiety, might aggravate his condition. If, on the other hand, he is kept in ignorance, his state and recuperation are dependent solely on his natural reserves untrammeled by useless fears and neuroses. This, in the long run, can only benefit him.

In my own case, I believe the doctors acted wisely. Though Eileen was under stresss and strain for weeks—and I fully appreciate what she endured—I was able to live a normal life for the next twelve years. And she, too, gradually came to accept that I was well again and there was no need to worry.

My annual visits to Professor Schrire were reassuring. He considered I had made a remarkable recovery while I scarcely gave the 1955 attack another thought. As a fatalist, I lived in, and for, the present, not in the past. I believed, in spite of my mother's fatal heart attack, that I was one of the fortunates who had had a "warning" which had not been repeated or developed into anything serious.

In January, 1967, the picture changed. I began to feel tired and exhausted. Work became a burden. With each day that passed I needed more rest at home and between tending patients. During the lunch hour I would relax in my dental chair, yet in the afternoon it required a strenuous effort to continue.

Still, I did not suspect the condition might be due to a failing heart. The attack I had occurred so long ago. And had I not been assured it was a light one? My tablets remained unused. I ascribed my state to overwork or, perhaps, it was age. I was getting on in years. Perhaps at fifty-eight I could not take it as I used to.

Getting up in the mornings became increasingly difficult. I felt as though I had been drugged when I dragged myself to the bathroom to shave and bathe. It had been my habit to commute by train to Cape Town. I would walk to the station, about ten minutes from my home in Rondebosch, and stroll back again in the late afternoon. I found even this short distance too much for me. I used the car to and from the station each day.

Every morning I had fits of coughing due to the accumulation of phlegm and fluid in my lungs. In spite of the discomfort I hoped, or tried to believe, it was a passing phase. Perhaps a holiday would help. Taking a week off, I drove to Great Brak River, about two hundred miles from Cape Town, and registered at a motel. Most of the time I spent miserably in bed. The drives there and back were a nightmare. In the light of later events, I am surprised I did not suffer another coronary attack at the wheel.

On my return, I resumed the daily struggle. I had to postpone appointments. I no longer spent the weekends at the beach, swimming and lazing in the sun. I needed them for rest, to gather strength for the week ahead. I decided to consult Professor Schrire, but he was on a lecture tour of the United States. I would carry on, I told myself, until he returned.

Sunday, March 5, 1967, is a day that will forever remain in my memory. I rested most of the time and, with Eileen, attended the wedding of a friend's daughter that night. We enjoyed ourselves immensely. I was feeling well, and we danced for the first time since our son's death six years before.

At about midnight I volunteered to drive some Pretoria friends to their hotel at St. James, on the False Bay coast, a journey of about forty miles there and back. We went to bed in the small hours. I was not unduly tired and believed the coming week would be less of a trial and ordeal.

When I wakened I had my usual spell of coughing, but this time it seemed to be even more acute. I struggled for breath and was on the verge of collapse.

"Eileen," I cried. "I can't carry on. I'm finished."

My doctor arrived within minutes. He examined me, gave me a palliative diuretic injection to filter off the fluid from my lungs, and ordered me to Groote Schuur Hospital by ambulance. Eileen accompanied me. I was examined by the admissions officer, Dr. Louis Sanders, and another physician who took an electrocardiogram. Dr. Sanders was of the opinion that I had had a coronary attack, but the two doctors did not agree. Nevertheless I was taken to medical ward D 1 and put to bed for observation and rest until Professor Schrire's return. To complicate matters, I contracted a urinary infection, but treatment soon cured it.

Professor Schrire arrived back shortly afterward and diagnosed that I had had a silent coronary thrombosis, if not a series, before I was brought to hospital. When I heard his verdict, I realized it would be a considerable time before I could resume my dental practice, if at all, and decided to sell it. It galled me though that my wife would have to continue working while I sat at home— she had, in fact, been employed by an electrical firm since my first attack in 1955—but it had to be faced. We also had to consider selling the home in which we had lived for twenty-one years. It would now be too big for two people; Jill was then in Israel.

One day Eileen walked into my ward and said, "Guess what! I've sold the house." I was overjoyed, for though she had always disliked the idea of living in an apartment, she now appeared to be reconciled to it. It would certainly lessen her burden.

During a seven week period in the hospital, I was subjected to numerous tests to aid Professor Schrire and his colleagues to arrive at a firm diagnosis and decide on the most suitable treatment. For me, the most interesting of all was to watch on closed circuit television an angiogram investigation, or heart geography, conducted by Dr. W. Beck, the cardiologist, and his team of assistants— two doctors, three nurses and three technicians. The object was to send the results to Dr. De Bakey, the world-renowned cardiologist in Texas, for his opinion on the advisability of performing the Vineberg operation on me.

This involves opening the chest, similar to the procedure adopted in an open heart operation, severing the internal mammary artery, a large blood vessel inside the breast bone, then anastomizing, or inserting, the end of the artery directly into the heart muscle; this affords an added supply of blood to the large vessel.

For the angiogram I was placed on an operating table, given a local anesthetic, and an incision was made on

53

the inside of the right elbow to reach a vein in the arm. The vein was pierced, a long catheter inserted, and slowly moved up to the region of the shoulder. There it took a left-hand turn and proceeded on its way to enter the heart chamber.

The head of the X-ray unit, resting about three inches above my chest, registered the position of the catheter and this, in turn, was transmitted to the TV circuit where it was visible to the surgeon and patient, me. More in fascination than in dread, I watched whether the catheter, manipulated at the elbow, would enter the different vessels of my heart. An opaque dye was also injected into my blood stream to establish whether the heart vessels were blocked or not; this injection was immediately followed by a warm glow through the vascular system, including the feet, and lasted a few seconds as it rapidly circulated through the body.

The surgeon's observations were taped on a recorder and a movie camera photographed the pictures thrown on the TV screen. Recordings were also taken on the electrocardiograph machine, the intracardiac blood pressure noted by the technicians, and all were meticulously described by the surgeon and taped.

The investigation and observations lasted for more than three hours but, in spite of my uncomfortable position on the table, I scarcely noticed the passing of time. I could barely wait for my wife's visit that afternoon to tell her of the wonders of medical science that had probed and tested the secrets of my heart for a cardiologist, thousands of miles away, to study in minute detail.

The taped recordings and pictures captured by the camera from the TV screen were mailed to Dr. De Bakey. Two months later he gave his opinion. He did not consider the Vineberg operation suitable in my case, a conclusion Professor Schrire had already reached from the data available to him.*

Once again, it seemed, destiny intended me for something different.

On my discharge from the hospital, I felt somewhat better for the rest and treatment. Professor Schrire, however, was noncommittal. He assured me that, with rest, the heart's recuperative powers were great but depended on its reserves. After a year's rest at home, according to him, I would probably be able to do "light" work again. I felt comforted. It could have been worse. As it happened, I rallied so much in the next few months that I believed, in optimistic moments, I would surprise the doctors and make a complete recovery.

But to Eileen, Professor Schrire had admitted my condition was bad, and, once more, she was warned to expect the worst.

"Let your husband do anything he wishes," he told her. "Let him drive his car and eat and drink what he likes. I am afraid his days are numbered."

Again she had to live with her grim secret. Not for a moment did I realize, when she returned home from work each evening, that her bright smile and words of encouragement, her light chatter about the events of the day, were all part of an act inspired by an iron determination not to break down and reveal the truth.

I spent my time resting and reading, going to the

---

* The first man to insert a catheter in a blood vessel and into the heart was a German, Dr. W. Forsmann, who, in 1929, guided one into his own heart and walked down two flights of stairs to show his colleagues. They considered his act "lunacy." His feat remained a surgical curiosity for many years until it was adopted by an American cardiologist to aid him in the diagnosis of cardiac conditions. Since then it has been used as a matter of routine by cardiologists the world over.

movies in the afternoon, driving to the beaches. It was a frustrating and exasperating existence. At the back of my mind, too, was the gnawing anxiety about my financial position. I had sold my practice and home and had a certain amount of capital. But how long would I be able to live on it? Would I *ever* be able to work again? What would happen to Eileen and Jill if I could not, if I became a chronic invalid, a burden on them?

At one time I considered becoming a medical representative, if I could not resume my profession, but the deterioration which now overtook me made even that possibility fade. From September, 1967, onward I spent more time in bed than out of it. By then we had moved into our apartment at Highbury, Wynberg, a suburb several miles from Rondebosch. I became weaker by the day. I gasped for breath, and the coughing spells racked me more than before. Professor Schrire prescribed still larger doses of diuretics to filter off the ever-increasing fluid in my lungs. I took as many as eight (320 milligrams) a day.

So it went on until December 3, the day that was to change so many lives and write new pages into medical history. It was the day the world learned that 45-year-old Professor Christiaan N. Barnard, head of a specially trained and selected team, had transplanted a new heart, taken from a car accident victim, Denise Darvall, into Louis Washkansky, a sufferer like myself.

I was feeling particularly ill and despondent at the time, but when I heard the momentous news over the radio at the lunch hour I called Eileen. She hurried to the bedroom to find me wildly excited.

"Did you hear the news?" I asked her.

"No, what news?" she said.

"A man," I said, "has been given a new heart. Right

here in Cape Town, in the Groote Schuur Hospital. His name is Louis Washkansky. Isn't that terrific?" At first, I thought, the implications of the operation did not seem to register with her.

Let her take up the story of the events of that day:

"I thought Phil's remark interesting, but somehow I could not comprehend exactly what had happened. Though I knew he was desperately ill, I had no thought that he could also be given a new heart and he certainly didn't mention it. But he remained excited and said he hoped Louis Washkansky would pull through. He just could not stop talking about it.

"By four o'clock, however, he was so ill that I was more anxious than usual. I had never telephoned Professor Schrire directly before, but I believed a call was warranted now. He walked in while I was talking to his wife. He took the receiver from her and inquired what was the matter. I replied that Phil was very ill indeed. He asked whether I had not received his message—that he had told our family doctor Phil was being considered for a second heart transplant. It appeared later that our doctor had telephoned several times but he had missed me.

"Anyhow, Professor Schrire repeated that Phil was next on the list. I was astounded. All I could manage to blurt out was 'This is stupendous' or something like that. Then I recalled the remark he had made about three months previously but which I had, naturally, kept from Phil. Short of a *new* heart, nothing could help or save him. At the time I thought Professor Schrire was being oddly facetious, and I ventured to tell him so. He replied he had not been joking but was in deep earnest.

"There were several visitors in our apartment at the time, and I told them of the conversation. I was shaking with excitement and could barely control myself. Suddenly, miraculously, there seemed to be a chance of saving Phil. Each morning I had been used to waking up with the thought—how long will he still be with me? Would I, perhaps, get an urgent call at the office that. . . . Now there was a glimmer of hope.

"But I did not know how to break the news to Phil—yet. He was too ill to see our guests. In fact, it was one of the worst days he had had but for his brief period of excitement and pleasure at the success of the operation on Louis Washkansky.

"At six o'clock he told me he was very depressed and could go on no longer. He recalled bitterly that he had talked to his doctors about what he planned to do after his recovery. Now he realized they must have thought him a fool to speak as he had—he, a dying man.

"I realized this was the opportunity to tell him of a prospect that had seemed quite beyond the realms of possibility.

" 'Phil,' I said, 'what would you say if they offered you a new heart like Louis Washkansky?'

"He stretched out his arms. 'I would go mad with excitement,' he exclaimed. 'The sooner the better.' He made me promise that, whatever the outcome of the Washkansky transplant, I would 'stay with him all the way.' Of course I would, I said. And there we were, two people, married for over thirty years and with a grown-up daughter, suddenly laughing and crying like children."

Now, for the first time, I realized I was dying as Louis Washkansky had been. I tried to prepare Eileen for the inevitable, unaware that she had known the truth all along, that she had worn a smile to hide her fears. Yet, in spite of my words, blunt but tinged with what comfort I could convey, she kept up the pretence.

"Phil," she said, "don't talk nonsense. You'll get better even though it might take a while yet."

Her words annoyed me. This was no time, I felt, for illusions, so-called "brave talk" or false hopes. Grim as the prospects were, we had to face them like sensible people, like men and women of the world. To humor me, she agreed to summon my attorney to add a codicil to my will (in which I left my clothing to our maid) and draw up a power of attorney as I insisted the time had arrived for her to handle my affairs on her own.

I thought things over as calmly and rationally as I could. I must not bluff myself with optimistic daydreams, but deal with realities. In spite of the promise and prospect of a transplant, which might save me, I believed there were too many obstacles to overcome. A suitable donor would have to be found. By an amazing coincidence and heartrending tragedy, a donor had been provided for Louis Washkansky at the eleventh hour. Would that also happen in my case? And if it did, he would have to be cross-matched with me in blood grouping and tissue-typing compatibility.

These were obstacles that might, probably would, prove insurmountable in the time I had left on this earth. I accepted the fact, fatalist that I was, that I would not survive. My suffering would be over though it would be hard on Eileen and Jill. We had been a devoted and happy family, but perhaps there was a reason why Fate was about to shatter our lives.

Eileen did not give up hope. As before, she refused to accept the inevitable. She continually asked Professor Schrire when the operation could be performed. He advised her to be patient; the condition and progress of Louis Washkansky had to be watched. But how could she be patient when she saw me sinking day by day? She told Professor Schrire I was dying.

It was finally arranged that I would be admitted to Groote Schuur Hospital on December 16, 1967, a public holiday, when, it was hoped, I could be smuggled in without fuss or publicity. The hospital, at the time, was bedlam. The successful Washkansky operation had gripped the imagination of the world. Television and radio teams and special correspondents from newspapers and magazines abroad had flown to Cape Town to satisfy an insatiable appetite for news of the first man to live with a new heart in his breast.

The news hawks resorted to any ruse for scoops. They had unlimited expense accounts, instructions to buy and pay anything for a "beat" on their competitors. Professor Barnard and Professor Schrire and other members of the transplant team were overwhelmed. The routine at the hospital was affected.

Word somehow got about that a second heart transplant was imminent. It was the last thing Groote Schuur wanted known with the chaos existing. We did our best to keep my name secret. But tongues wagged. A "retired dentist," it was said, was being considered, and the transplant team had been placed on stand-by once more. By a process of elimination, the Press ferreted out that I was to be *that* patient. The headlines rivaled those of the Washkansky story.

My wife, like her relatives and friends, was given no rest or peace by day or night. The telephone was jammed with local and overseas calls, from the U.S., England, Australia, everywhere. She was driven frantic. But, like the doctors and hospital authorities, she refused to talk.

The news hunt went on as the story snowballed. Confirmation that I was soon to undergo the operation and, more important, the date, appeared to be the only news editors wanted. Wars, floods, and other disasters took second place. I became the most talked-of man in the world, it seemed.

December 16 still remained the proposed day of admission though it was top secret. Eileen and doctors spoke vaguely on the telephone in case the line was tapped. But newsmen and TV teams maintained a constant vigil outside our apartment and at Groote Schuur to insure that I was not moved without their knowledge. When Eileen refused to produce a photograph of me, it was learned I had played rugby for the Royal Dental Hospital in London. A picture, taken with my team about thirty-five years before, was rooted out and radioed all over the world.

A further worsening in my condition precipitated matters. The date had to be advanced. I had such a bad turn on the afternoon of December 14 that Eileen summoned Dr. Kohn as well as Dr. Marcus Getz, who lived nearby, to examine me. They decided the position was desperate and that I should be taken to the hospital immediately for palliative treatment and oxygen to help me breathe.

I was only vaguely aware of what was going on around me, of the fierce publicity spotlight trained on my flat, and the arrangements for a transplant in the event of a suitable donor being found in time. While plans were made to save my life, I could think of little but death, which seemed preferable to life as I had been living it.

All I wanted was relief in whatever form it came. I was at the end of my tether. I inhaled oxygen periodically by face mask. It proved of little use. Palliative injections to help me breathe were no better. I gasped for air like a fish out of water as treatment became less and less effective. Any bodily effort or movement was an unendurable strain. My mental faculties became sluggish due to the impaired circulation caused by my failing heart.

Oh, I thought to myself again, for an end to it all! If it meant death, I would welcome it. If, on the other hand, the promised operation was successful, so much the better, but now I had scant hope that I would last that long.

Death has never held any terrors for me. If I reached the operating theater and passed out there it would, I reasoned, be a form of indirect euthanasia. And while on the subject of death, and my nearness to it, might I add my views on cremation? I consider the old-fashioned manner and idea of burial barbaric, apart from being wasteful. Valuable land that is used for cemeteries could be better utilized for erecting homes and apartment buildings, swimming pools, playing fields, and parks for the living and the healthy.

Though often mentally dulled, I took an interest in Louis Washkansky's progress. I learned from fellow patients, radio bulletins, and occasionally glancing at the headlines, that he was improving and seemed to have every hope of recovery. I was happy for him and his wife and wondered again whether I would live long enough to be his successor.

4

ENTER DOCTOR BARNARD

The day after my admission to Ward D 1, I was lying in bed with eyes closed, feeling drowsy and thoroughly miserable when I sensed someone at the head of my bed. I opened my eyes and saw a man. He was tall, young, good-looking with features that reminded me a lot of General Jan Christian Smuts in his latter years. His hands were beautiful; the hands of the born surgeon.

"Don't you know me?" he asked.

"No," I said with little interest, "I don't."

"I'm Professor Chris Barnard," he said.

"I'm sorry, Professor," I replied, "but I didn't recognize you. I have never seen you in person, and you look so different from your photographs in the Press."

He spoke earnestly. "Dr. Blaiberg, how do you feel about the prospect of a heart transplant operation? You probably know, don't you, that I am prepared to do you next?"

"The sooner the better," I said fervently, "and I promise you my full cooperation at all times."

Though our conversation was brief and he stayed only a few minutes, I was immediately impressed with the stature of the man and his air of buoyant optimism. He inspired me with the greatest confidence, an invaluable asset in the relations between a surgeon and his patient.

I felt somewhat better. Here was a man to whom I

would willingly entrust my life. I came to know him well in the weeks and months that followed. He is a vital, determined, somewhat mercurial, personality, utterly dedicated to his profession.

Geniuses are not like ordinary people. You have to forgive them their tantrums, irritability, ill temper and dogmatism. Some of those who have come in close touch with Barnard and experienced these facets of his character know he can be as charming as he is sometimes grim, as lovable as he is occasionally offhand, as wryly humorous as he can be impatient, as willing to listen as to be dogmatic. They know no one with greater grit and resolution, willing to do more for his patients, rich or poor, well-born or humble, White or non-White. He strives for them, suffers with them, devotes himself entirely to them. That is how I found him. I am proud to have been called the "most famous" patient of one who has gained international renown and is now an outstanding heart surgeon of our time.

Today, as I reflect on that historic meeting between a dying man and one who will live in the annals of medical history as long as Lister, Pasteur, and Eve Curie, many stories of Chris Barnard come to mind.

Son of a poor Dutch Reformed Church missionary in the village of Beaufort West (Cape Province), he played rugby barefoot because he had no football boots, and was drenched to the skin as he walked in the rain to the university in Cape Town, when he could not afford the train fare, he is now met at airports with special protocol, entertained by Presidents and Prime Ministers and the world's leading surgeons. His name is a household one in the United States, South Africa, Europe, and the Orient. He could have any position he chooses at a fabulous salary, but he prefers to serve his cause and people in South Africa.

His arrival in New York these days is an event though a comparatively few years ago, in 1955—when by coincidence I had my first heart attack—he was unknown, and there was no one to welcome him. As he flew from London to New York on his way to the University of Minnesota in Minneapolis, where he was to do research, he had, he recalls, "a terrible feeling that he was in an enormous current or uncontrollable force, which dragged him along and over which he had no control." He wondered whether he had done the right thing, leaving his wife and family to spend several years in a foreign land.

I prefer to think the "enormous current" and "uncontrollable force" was a high destiny leading him to his fame and triumphs. And it was my destiny that our lives should eventually be interwoven.

His first experience of New York had its amusing side. He had to take a plane to Minneapolis, and it was necessary to change his money into dollars. He did not know the rate of exchange nor how many dollars he would get for £1. In fact, one, five, and ten dollar bills looked all the same to him as he fumbled with them.

A porter grabbed his portmanteau, threw it on a trolley and pushed it along. Barnard wanted to carry it himself. Besides, he was worried about a tip. He had no money to spare but was afraid of offending the porter.

When his luggage was dumped, he pulled out a bill and handed it over. The porter glanced at it, first with puzzlement, then with evident satisfaction, and scurried off.

It did not take Barnard long to learn the reason for the

porter's eagerness to disappear as quickly as he could. He had been given a ten dollar tip and, fearing the mistake would be noticed, left also with Barnard's overcoat, the first he owned, bought in London a day or two before.

Barnard overtook him. "Listen," he said, "I'm a stranger here, and I've made a mistake. I only wanted to give you a dollar bill." He held out one.

The porter looked at Barnard more in pity than in anger. But he must have seen the distress in his face and what ten dollars meant to him.

"Sure, I've got the ten dollar bill," he said, handing it over to a grateful Barnard. He also returned the precious overcoat.

In Minneapolis, he had been given an address to telephone in case of difficulty. But the dialing system was different from the one he knew in Cape Town. He approached a man for help.

"Use dimes and nickels," the man said. Barnard did not know the difference.

"Here, let me show you." The man identified the coins. Barnard selected the dimes and nickels and dialed the number. A pleasant, friendly voice answered. Arrangements were made to fetch him from the airport.

Barnard has never been ashamed of his poverty and humble beginnings, earning money the hard way. As a schoolboy he sold bags, bottles, and bones and caddied to make a few pennies pocket money. When he was doing research work and preparing an important thesis at the University of Minnesota, his wife and children joined him from South Africa. He rented an apartment before their arrival in Minneapolis and set about earning the money, in his limited spare time, to furnish it. He mowed lawns, washed cars, acted as a "special" for patients at night, and worked in a cafeteria collecting dishes and carting them to the kitchen. The dollars mounted, and gradually the apartment was furnished— even to a television set, a toy train and cowboy suit for his little son, Andre, and toys for his daughter, Deidre.

On the morning of December 21, 1967, I was surprised to see my wife walk into my ward at about 9:30. Her visits had always been in the afternoons because of her morning job.

"Aren't you working today?" I asked.

"No," she said. "I just felt I wanted to see you."

"The nurses have told me that Professor Barnard is also coming to see me this morning," I said.

It seemed strange and unusual, but I did not give the matter further thought. I accepted Eileen's explanation and believed Professor Barnard's visit would be mere routine. Soon afterward he walked in. Eileen rose to excuse herself.

"No, don't go," Professor Barnard said to her. "I want to speak to you together." I looked more closely at him. He was haggard and drawn as though he had not slept all night. He no longer resembled the handsome Smuts, to whom I had compared him, but more a martyred Christ. I felt a twinge of pity for him when I noticed the pain in his face and eyes. Something, I was sure, had happened to dampen the gaiety and boundless optimism I had seen before.

Eileen already knew that Louis Washkansky had died earlier that morning. I did not. Nurses and my fellow patients had been instructed to withhold the news from me as it was thought the shock would be too much. As it happened, however, I was feeling so tired, despondent, and disinterested in everything about me that I had not inquired, as I usually did, how Louis Washkansky was progressing. So I knew nothing.

Professor Barnard spoke in low tones. "I feel like a pilot who has just crashed," he said. "Now I want you, Dr. Blaiberg, to help me by taking up another plane as soon as possible to get back my confidence."

Still I did not know what he was driving at. "Professor," I said, puzzled, "why are you telling me this? You know I am prepared to undergo a heart transplant operation at any time you wish."

"But don't you know that Louis Washkansky is dead?" he asked. "He died this morning, of pneumonia."

It dawned on me why Eileen and Professor Barnard had paid me this unexpected visit. Now I knew the reason for his distress and agitation.

"Professor Barnard," I said at once, "I want to go through with it now more than ever—not only for my sake but for you and your team who put so much into your effort to save Louis Washkansky."

I was more upset and sorry than I could say for all those who had helped in the miracle which had ended in tragedy. A great pity welled up in me for Ann Washkansky who had passed through an ordeal such as is experienced by few wives. My remarks apparently lessened Professor Barnard's distress.

"Don't worry," he said a little more cheerfully now, "everything is going to be fine."

During the next few days I was visited by two other members of the transplant team—immunologist Dr. M. C. Botha, Pathologist-in-Charge, Cape Provincial Blood Grouping Laboratory, and Dr. S. C. W. Bosman of the Department of Surgery, Groote Schuur Hospital.

One evening, I remember, my brother-in-law, Abe Abel, came to the ward. He had heard of my decision to undergo the operation and wanted a final word with me.

"Phil," he said, "the time of the operation is drawing near. If you feel you don't want to go through with it, don't be shy. There is still time to back out. After all, it's *your* life."

"Abe," I said, "I have made up my mind, and there is no question of changing it or turning back."

"Well," he repeated, "I only wanted to warn you to be quite sure."

"I have never been surer of anything," I said firmly. "I want to have a change of life with a transplant. Otherwise life will not be worth living."

As I continued to sink from day to day I was moved from the general ward I shared with about twenty other patients, to the three-bed intensive cardiac unit where it was quieter and more restful. I was not there long before I was moved to Ward C 2 to occupy a room to myself in the cardiac section. Here two nurses arrived to shave my entire body in preparation for the operation which, I realized, was now imminent.

Instead of using clippers and an electric razor, which would have been quicker and easier on my hirsute body, they applied a safety razor. It was a slow and laborious process and not unattended by a few nicks of the skin. But I had had to endure far worse in recent weeks. I accepted it as just one more, but minor, inconvenience to be borne.

The cardiac team stood by again in the event of a suitable donor becoming available. Professor Barnard realized time was the all-important factor if I were to have a chance. My appetite, which had always been good, had diminished to the vanishing point. My usual weight was about 175 pounds; now it was 155 pounds. I had a constant, raging thirst, yet I was limited to about four glasses of water and other liquids a day in order to assist my failing heart, already sufficiently burdened with its function of pumping blood through the circulatory system.

While I was at my lowest ebb, the long arm of coincidence was about to stretch out from Groote Schuur Hospital across Cape Town's sprawling southern suburbs to the tiny strip of Glencairn beach, about twenty miles away, on the False Bay coast.

It was New Year's Day, 1968, a public holiday in South Africa and midsummer. Everyone in Cape Town was on vacation. The beaches were packed with holiday-makers tanning themselves in the hot sunshine, splashing happily in the cool waves.

New Year's Day, and the following day, also a public holiday for most workers in the Cape, belong traditionally to the Colored folk. Clad in gaily colored raiment, merrily strumming their guitars and singing their tuneful folksongs interspersed with the latest bop hits, they swing through the city streets for their annual Minstrel Carnival. Large crowds gather to watch and cheer their capers. For Clive and Dorothy Haupt the New Year Day's treat was to be a trip to Glencairn beach with friends and members of their family. They packed a large picnic basket and set out early to laze in the sun, play on the sands, and swim in the sea.

Clive Haupt was born on October 16, 1943, one of eleven children of a poor Colored family who lived in a small two-bedroom cottage in Q Town, Athlone, a

72

large Colored township which forms a suburb of Cape Town.

To the casual observer, the small barefooted lad playing in the Athlone streets was no different from thousands like him. But to his mother, Mrs. Muriel Haupt, he was. From an early age he showed qualities her other children did not. She brought them up well and all were obedient. But Clive, she felt, was a cut above them. He was "specially good."

Certainly he would rough and tumble with the boys. And he was not scared to stand up to someone who wanted to start a fight. But he was considerate where others were thoughtless, mannerly where others were careless. He was peace-loving where others were quarrelsome. These qualities endeared him to everyone. He never sought to push himself. He was not a leader and kept quietly to himself.

When he reached Standard Six he left the North Primary School, Athlone. He had the ability to study further, but it was difficult for his mother, then a widow, to rear her large family. She needed every penny to ward off starvation. So Clive went out to look for work.

He was sixteen when he started his first job at a factory which manufactured breakfast foods. He worked there for three years, then at a nylon and spinning factory where he was a machinist.

He had few girl friends. Then he met Dorothy Snyders, a girl of his own age. She was also shy and retiring, and their tastes and interests were alike. They would attend the movies or spend the evenings at home playing cards.

They had been courting about a year before they became engaged. The big day was August 13, 1966,

Dorothy's birthday. A year later they married in St. Luke's Anglican Church, and Clive moved from his own home to Dorothy's large house in Portland Street, Salt River, opposite the church.

On holidays friends would call for Clive and Dorothy, who could not afford a car, and take them for drives into the country or to the beach. That was how they came to be at Glencairn that New Year's Day, 1968.

The hours on the beach passed pleasantly. At noon someone started to throw a ball about. Clive joined in with zest. Laughingly, he dived at his wife's legs. Next moment he lay motionless. "He must have gone to sleep," an onlooker laughed. Others said he was fooling. Clive liked a practical joke.

But his wife quickly sensed that something was wrong. She ran to him and turned him over. He was unconscious. His tongue and mouth were swollen and he frothed at the mouth. He was hurried by car to the nearest hospital, at False Bay. Doctors summoned an ambulance to take him to the larger Victoria Hospital, in the suburb of Wynberg. His breathing was weak when he reached there at 3:30 p.m.—three and a half hours after his collapse on the beach.

Dr. Basil Sacks, an intern, who examined him, was impressed with his apparent physical fitness and youth. Diagnosing a massive cerebral hemorrhage, he observed that the man's breathing was becoming progressively worse. Ten minutes later it stopped. This sign of respiratory failure indicated irreversible brain damage and death seemed imminent.

As a last resort, Dr. Sacks placed a tube down the man's throat and breathed for him artificially. He was assisted by Dr. J. Filmer who was also on duty. What impressed the doctors was the manner in which the heart

74

began to beat with the application of oxygen. They expected it to continue, however, for only a brief period under artificial respiration. Once his breathing ceased, nothing could be done to save him. But, they reasoned, his heart must be extremely strong for it to have reacted in the way it did.

Dr. Sacks telephoned Dr. Coert Venter, senior registrar of Ward C2 at Groote Schuur Hospital. "I might have a heart donor for you," he said and described Haupt's condition. He knew a second transplant was imminent and that a donor was being sought.

Five minutes later Dr. Venter was on the telephone. He urged the doctors to do their utmost to keep the patient alive and bring him to Groote Schuur with all speed. Dr. Sacks accompanied Haupt in the ambulance giving him artificial respiration on the way by ambu bag. With him was a blood sample Dr. Venter had asked him to take before putting up an intravenous drip. This blood was to be used for cross-matching purposes to determine whether it was compatible with mine.

The team had gathered in readiness at the hospital when the ambulance arrived shortly after 5 p.m., and the battle for Clive Haupt's life continued. Dorothy Haupt, her mother, and Mrs. Muriel Haupt, Clive's mother, sat in a room waiting in anguish for news.

At 7 p.m. it came. Dr. Venter told Dorothy her husband's condition was critical. The doctors were still fighting to save him, but there was little they could do. An artery had burst in his brain. It was Dr. Venter's lot to ask her whether she would consent to her husband's heart being used in a transplant operation.

Transplant? Her husband dying when only a few short hours before he had been happily picnicking on the beach? It seemed unreal.

At first the words did not come. She was overwhelmed. Then she sobbed, "If you can save someone else's life in that way, you may take my husband's heart."

She walked over and spoke to Clive's mother. Would she likewise agree to the removal of her son's heart to save a dying man? Her reply, too, was yes.

Tests continued. Led by Dr. Botha, the team's immunologist, doctors checked their early diagnosis that Clive Haupt's heart would be suitable for transplantation. A cardiac monitor noted its every beat. Matching tests involving factors for tissue-typing were started.

At 9 p.m. it was decided to reassess the prognosis later. Clive would die if artificial breathing were stopped. But that in itself was a form of treatment. It would be continued until there was no hope at all of life.

It was an agonizing night for the Haupt family and a tense and anxious one for the transplant team who stood by for a call that might come at any moment.

Yet another twelve hours were to pass before the operation.

Those who believe numbers have some significance in our lives may be impressed by the part the figure 2 played in Clive Haupt's life and death.

He was the second eldest child. He died on the second day of January, the second in his family to die. His father was the first. He was donor for the second heart transplant. And on the second night after his death his mother had a strange dream which came true.

In the dream, Clive spoke to her and said, "Mother, I looked after you while you were alive. Now that I am dead, do not worry. You will never be in want again."

Mrs. Haupt's rent is now paid regularly each month

by an anonymous woman donor. "I wish I knew who she was," Mrs. Haupt says. "I would like to thank her."

I did not learn till later of these developments and my memories of what happened on New Year's Day and night are blurred today. So let Eileen take up the story:

"I happened to be visiting Phil on the afternoon of January 1, but, for the first time, he slept practically continuously. I remained on till seven o'clock waiting for him to awaken when Dr. Bosman called me to the doctors' waiting room. The operation on Phil, he said, would probably take place within the next few hours. I greeted the news with a mixture of excitement and relief. At last the suspense I had endured and the fears and despair of the past few weeks would be ended for me. I had learned, as they say, to 'live with it,' but there are limits.

"Nothing was told to me about a donor, and I did not ask. I gathered they probably did not want me to know at that stage. But I noticed a family of Colored people waiting anxiously in the passage and wondered whether they were, perhaps, connected with the donor. In a nearby room I watched doctors working frantically to save a man's life. What agony I went through. Was Phil's life to depend on his death or survival?

"Back I went to the doctors' room to inquire whether they intended telling Phil about the probable time of the operation. They replied they would rather leave it until a later hour. I returned to Phil's ward to keep him company. He soon noticed that the water and tablets that were usually at his bedside had vanished. He was fuming. He had saved the largest quantity of the water permitted him. Now it was gone. What was it all about?

77

"I didn't know how to talk myself out of that one but fortunately, at that moment, Dr. Bosman walked in. 'I want my water back immediately,' Phil said. 'This is not the right thing to do to me, really.'

"Dr. Bosman grinned. 'Well, Phil,' he said, 'I wasn't going to tell you till later. But as I can see you are going to nag us, I will. The operation will take place, we believe, by eleven o'clock. Now you know why you can't have any water, no matter how thirsty you are.'

"A look of delight came over Phil's face such as I had not seen since his illness began in March. 'At last you rogues are going to do something,' he said. 'I thought the day would never arrive.'

"I was left alone in the ward with Phil. He could not relax for a moment and became more and more worked up. The transplant team had, by then, gathered in the waiting room opposite Phil's ward. I asked them whether it would not be advisable to give him a sedative to calm him down. Calm *him* down! The doctors seemed to be as excited as Phil; there was a feeling of tension that I did not think possible among members of the medical profession, used as they are to daily crises. Perhaps the reason was the knowledge that the experience gained and the lessons learned in the Washkansky case could now be applied with hope of greater success.

"Phil was given heavy sedation and within half an hour he was fast asleep and did not awaken until 9:30 the next morning. Before he dozed off he asked me to stay with him until the operation. I was not prepared for a night's vigil at the hospital. So, while he slept, I went home for a coat and to tell my family The Moment had arrived.

"I did not know whether I was more excited or worried. My mind was in a whirl. I was back at Groote

Schuur at eight o'clock and sat beside Phil, as I had promised, leaving him intermittently for coffee. I must have drunk twenty cups as the hours dragged by.

"Throughout the night the hospital was surrounded by TV men and journalists. How they got wind of the impending operation only they know. But I have learned, from experience, you can't keep a story from men with a nose for news. They refused to accept vague statements. Nurses had to order them from the passage where Phil's and the donor's wards were located. They were threatened with the police. Still they prowled about. Telephone calls were booked to London and New York to catch the latest editions of newspapers.

"For me, though, it was no story, no matter what impact it made on the world. It was my husband's life. The hours had never passed so slowly. Eleven o'clock came and went. Then it was midnight. Still there was no word to relieve my suspense.

"Members of my family visited me continually, but I could tell them nothing definite. At three o'clock in the morning, a doctor assured me that it would be pointless to remain at the hospital any longer. The operation, it appeared, was still many hours off. Members of the transplant team had returned home to snatch a few hours' sleep but were on call at a moment's notice.

"In spite of my protests, a house doctor drove me home. I would benefit from a little sleep, he said. Sleep! How I could have done with it, but even at 3:15 a.m., when I reached my apartment, sleep was far away. How I envied my neighbors their peaceful slumbers. I took pen and paper and wrote to Jill to tell her the operation was due that morning. She read about it in the Israeli newspapers before my letter reached her.

"Exhausted, I threw myself on the bed. It was 5:30. I

fell into a troubled sleep. At 9:30 the telephone rang. I was wanted at hospital immediately, a voice said. I felt numbed. I could not think or feel anything. All I knew was that I had to get to Groote Schuur as soon as possible.

"I found Phil about to be put on a trolley and taken to the operating theater. What amazed me was the complete composure and delight on his face at such a moment. We said good-by to each other without emotion. But as he was wheeled out of sight, I broke down completely. I cried as though my heart would break.

"The realization suddenly came to me that a momentous event was about to take place. Phil was to receive a new heart, but so had Louis Washkansky; now he was dead after eighteen days of fluctuating progress.

"I was worried sick in case it would prove to be the last time I saw Phil alive. For the first time I began to have doubts about the operation. Had I been right in encouraging him to undergo it when, in fact, he might die? That he had insisted on it brought me no comfort. If he died on the operating table, I told myself, I would never forgive myself. For even if he had only a few more days to live, I might have been responsible for his passing before his time. Why had I been placed in this terrible dilemma?

"I was taken home by taxi. All about me I saw holiday-makers, happy and carefree. They were enjoying themselves as they did every New Year. This, to them, was no different. They did not know or care—and why should they?—about the anguish I was suffering. Their world in 1968 would probably be the same for them. For me it was already crashing about my ears. I felt bitter.

"At home I found a powerful sleeping tablet my doctor had left for me. I swallowed it. It knocked me out completely for hours. I did not have to sit, agonizingly awake at the radio and telephone, like my sisters and brother, waiting for news. When I awakened, they told me of the news flash. The operation had been a complete success.

"Phil's new heart had started to beat without even an electric shock.

"What did I think of at that moment when I knew Phil's life had been spared, that my prayers had been answered, that the barest flicker of hope had been rekindled?

"At first I was too stunned to grasp the immensity and wonder of it. Then, gradually, the prospect and possibility of a future life together with Phil spread out before me. Can any of you imagine what a feeling of relief and gladness that was for a woman who had accepted, for nine months, that she would have to live the rest of her life without her loved one?

"My friends telephoned and crowded our apartment to celebrate. The champagne corks popped. They were delirious with joy and excitement and toasted me and Phil. They drank to his good health and many more years of life. I thanked them; but I told them it was not yet time for celebration, only thankfulness. I realized only too well, though I don't think they did at the time, the hazards that lay ahead.

"I remembered the excitement after the operation on Louis Washkansky and how tragically it ended. I was determined to remain level-headed, not to give way to overoptimism, to wait and see how things developed during the next few weeks.

"I did not know at that time that a comparatively easy passage lay before us. Every day I feared, or expected, some complication or setback. When I spoke to the doctors at the hospital they sounded elated and assured me all was well.

"I breathed a prayer of relief but said to myself, 'Eileen, just wait another few days before *you* get delirious about it all.' And that is just what I did. I knew that no one, not even the doctors, could predict the course of events in the next few days and weeks, the effects of the immuno-suppressive drugs. Anything could go wrong at any time. No one could give me any guarantees.

"Each day I awoke with the thought, 'What is today going to bring?'

"I did not know, or realize, till later, what a disruptive and devastating effect the blaze of publicity trained on Phil and the operation, was to have on our daughter, Jill, in Israel. She was quite unprepared for it and found it merciless and soulless.

"It was the last thing she wanted. She had been carefree and happy as Jill Blaiberg, a kibbutz volunteer, later a worker on a *moshav*, in the home of Mr. and A. Shavit, who treated her as their own daughter, and then a student at an ulpan for a five months' intensive course in Hebrew. Like so many others she had grown to love Israel and its life and her new friends.

"On the outbreak of the Six Day War in June, 1967, she was studying for a B.A. degree and Performer's Diploma in speech and drama at the University of Cape Town and had immediately volunteered to go to Israel.

"Phil was ill at the time, though Jill did not know how desperately, but he made no objection. Instead, he had a fierce pride in the fact that his daughter would join hundreds of other young Jews and Jewesses who, after the comparative luxury of life in South Africa, would rise at the crack of dawn to work on the land, milk cows, drive tractors, harvest crops, and do all the things he believed Jill would never want, or be prepared, to do.

"Because Jill and Phil have such strong characters and are so much alike, they had often clashed during her school days. She was a more than diligent pupil. She was intense and serious, too serious Phil thought, in her efforts to obtain outstanding results in class and examinations.

"Moderation in all things, happiness, healthy social sporting, and extramural activities were, to him, more important than the good results she was achieving.

"Her letters from Israel told him and me of the pleasure she was getting from a new sense of well-being by giving unselfishly of herself in every sphere in a land where she felt she belonged. She wrote of sharing a room with other girls, participating in sports, folk sing songs, and dancing, how she 'laughd into the sunset' as she drove a tractor, of the hard physical labor that was a delight and privilege instead of a burden. She was happy and so were we.

"Imagine the shock to her when she was shown a newspaper report that Phil might be the next patient for a heart transplant. She wondered why I had not told her myself in a letter. Later I was able to explain that I wanted to break the news to her, gently, and in my own way but the news hawks had got in first.

"There was irony in the way the publicity now affected her. For as long as she could remember, she had wanted to be a famous actress or ballerina with her name in lights. But shortly before she went to Israel, and while there, she had reached a stage in maturity when her sense of values mattered more to her than fame or popularity. Spiritual peace was now more important to her. The few good, honest friends she had, including her parents, were sufficient to make her world a happy one.

"Then, suddenly, without warning her world crashed. The fame, the publicity she had once wanted but no longer sought or cared about, was thrust on her. As the daughter of the only living heart transplant patient, one of the most talked-of men in the world, she, too, had to be a celebrity, whether she liked it or not, and endure the publicity that attended it.

"Journalists, television and radio teams flocked to interview and write about her. She was hounded day and night. Her privacy vanished. She found herself in the headlines, in magazines, on television screens. New 'friends' arrived by the hundred. Some meant well but, among them, she felt, were sensation-seekers and those who wanted to exploit her.

"They built up a public image of her as a young girl, as lovely and glamorous as a film star. It was not only an exaggerated picture, she felt, but one that was not humanly possible to live up to even had she wished. Letters streamed in. There were proposals of marriage, a film offer from Germany. All, it seemed, wanted to cash in on the publicity she did not want and had come to detest and dread. She was no longer a happy Israeli worker. She wanted solitude. Instead, she was pestered wherever she went.

"The publicity grew until she felt it was, as she described it, like a foghorn blasting in her ears. It became a wave that threatened to engulf her. Only now, months afterward, she says, can she grasp the significance of it all, marvel at the operation that saved her father's life.

"She told me, on her return to South Africa after completing her Hebrew course, that when Phil drove her in his car it was like old times. They were the same healthy father and daughter together again. It was a time of privacy and togetherness which they cherished. It made up for much of what she had gone through."

5

OPERATION TRANSPLANT

I slept blissfully throughout the operation, unaware of the furor it created throughout the world. Only later was I to learn that I had become, like Louis Washkansky, a central figure in one of the greatest medical achievements of all time, that radio and television programs on the five Continents had been interrupted to give millions of viewers the news and minute-by-minute reports of my progress.

The transplant has been described in technical detail by experts in innumerable scientific journals in many languages. As, however, their treatises are often incomprehensible to the layman. I will try to give a simpler account of what happened to me during the long hours I lay on the operating table. It is based on what was told me by surgeons, doctors, technicians, and others who took part in the great adventure to give me my new heart. For adventure it was, both for them and for me.

The story, of course, began long before I reached the operating theater. If I were to go back to the beginning, I would have to tell of the long, arduous years of research by medical men and scientists of many lands, especially of the research carried out at Groote Schuur Hospital and the Medical School of Cape Town University by the very man, Professor Barnard, who performed the great transplant feat—research that gave the team the knowledge and confidence which enabled it to undertake the operation with high hope of success.

But the story I am to tell here, of the transplant itself, begins from the time the team was placed on stand-by. There were altogether fifty-one members, men and women, each with an essential role to play. Stand-by meant they had to be instantly available round the clock. Wherever they were, whatever they were doing, they had to insure that they could be reached by telephone. The call might come at any moment. When it did, they would have to speed to the hospital and take up action stations for the tasks which long training and painstaking practice had enabled them to perform smoothly and efficiently.

Now the success of an operation for transplanting a heart, or any other tissue from one individual to another, is not a matter of surgery only, no matter how skillful or heroic. The transplanted organ must "take"; the body must accept the new tissue, not reject it.

The human body functions in a way that makes it reject all foreign protein, and human tissues are made of protein. A transplanted heart is, therefore, liable to be rejected by its new host, and ultimate failure will be the result no matter how skillfully surgeons perform the operation. Before a transplant can be undertaken therefore, not only must a donor organ be available, but tests be performed to assess the likelihood of rejection.

This rejection mechanism is the same as the immunity mechanism—the methods by which the body overcomes invading bacteria and viruses which are also all made of protein; in fact, the tissues of all living matter are made of protein.

When a germ invades the system, the body produces antibodies to the protein, of which the germ is made, and within a few days, these antibodies destroy or neutralize the invader. In many cases, these antibodies remain in the system for life. After an attack of measles, for instance, you remain immune to that particular disease for life. Whenever a measles virus enters the system, it is immediately destroyed by the antibodies.

This immunological process is the subject of intense and continual research, but we still cannot claim to understand fully how this mechanism achieves its results. We do know, however, that it is the lymphocytes— members of the white blood cells—that play a major role in producing these antibodies that reject or destroy protein.

As soon as the foreign matter enters the system, the lymphocytes make contact with it. They carry the message back to the lymph glands and other organs which manufacture these cells, "programing" these blood-forming organs to manufacture the required antibodies.

It takes a few days for this process to get under way, but in seven to ten days antibodies are being produced in sufficient quantity to deal with the foreign invader and to reject it. The foreign matter that sets the antibody-producing process in action is called an "antigen"; it "gen"erates the production of antibodies.

Even before the commonest transplant of all, a blood transfusion, is performed, it is necessary to make a few simple tests to insure the transfusion will not be rejected.

When tissues, such as heart or kidney, are transplanted, however, the tests are far more complicated that must be carried out to ascertain that the tissues of donor and recipient are as nearly compatible as possible. They are never completely compatible, but tissues from one individual may lead to a less pronounced rejection than those from another and, in that event, will be easier to suppress by the various means science has available.

Before any transplant operation can begin, therefore,

the blood groups of donor and recipient must be tested for compatibility. Samples of the lymphocytes are taken from each and tested for the presence of antigens—that is, proteins that stimulate the production of antibodies. Only when the results indicate a good chance of success can the operation proceed.

The tests performed on Clive Haupt and myself showed there was a reasonable chance that the immunological processes of rejection could be successfully controlled or even entirely suppressed by drugs and treatment after the operation.

And so the stage was set, all the actors in the drama waiting and ready to play their allotted parts. The result of the tests had given the team the "go ahead."

On the night of January 1, I had been given drugs that insured a good night's sleep. Next morning I had the usual sedatives a patient receives before surgical operations so that I was calm and relaxed. Indeed, I was barely awake and have no recollection of arriving in the operating theater.

Clive Haupt was already on the operating table in an adjoining theater, close to death. His breathing was maintained by means of a mechanical ventilation apparatus.

Most anesthetics for major operations these days begin with an injection of a solution of the drug pentothal into a vein. Within a few seconds this induces a feeling of pleasant sleepiness and, almost immediately it seems, you hear voices telling you to "wake up—it's all over."

After the anesthetist had injected a small quantity of the drug atropine into the vein—this dries up the secretions in the mouth, throat, and lungs insuring the air passages will remain free of sputum and mucous—he followed it up with pentothal, and I was almost immediately unconscious. He then passed a rubber tube through one nostril into the windpipe using an instrument called a laryngoscope which enabled him to see the vocal chords and insure the end of the tube was in exactly the right position.

This tube was connected up with the anesthetic machine with its cylinders of nitrous oxide—this used to be called laughing gas and is often used for dental anesthetics —and halothane. The effects of the pentothal injection soon wear off but, by that time, the patient is kept anesthetized by these two gases. The anesthetic machine allows the doctor to regulate the amount of gasses the patient is receiving, keeping him on an even keel of anesthesia, even "breathing" for him. All the while, doctors watch the level of the blood pressure, the pulse rate, the temperature, and administer additional drugs from time to time as required throughout the operation.

Most patients who undergo major surgery nowadays receive anesthetics in much the same way as I have so far described, making it a safe and smooth procedure with no discomfort.

In my case, however, the situation from this point on became much more complicated. In open-heart operations the heart is out of action for some of the time, but the circulation of blood must nevertheless be maintained even when the heart has been removed. The blood must deliver oxygen to the cells of all tissues of the body for them to sustain their life. It is especially important for the circulation to the brain to be maintained. If brain cells are deprived of oxygen for more than a minute or two they are damaged beyond repair.

The blood must, therefore, not only be circulated around the body but also through the lungs where it

91

collects oxygen and rids itself of that waste product, carbon dioxide.

For this purpose the heart-lung machine had been placed in readiness, and the doctors and technologists were already prepared to connect me with this apparatus, which would take over the work of the heart and lungs during the critical period.

Before the development of the heart-lung machine, operations which required the heart to be put out of action were virtually impossible. Surgeons who performed them had to complete their vital procedure within a minute or two, sometimes merely a matter of seconds, to allow the heart to resume its function.

Complicated as this apparatus is, the underlying principle is simple. The heart is a pump divided by a central partition into right and left sides, each having two chambers, an auricle and a ventricle; the auricles receive blood returning to the heart and the ventricles pump it outward.

The auricle of the right side receives blood returning from its trip round the body—blood which has given up its oxygen to the tissues and brought back carbon dioxide. The "impure" blood is carried into the auricle by two huge veins, the *venae cavae*. From the auricle the blood flows into the right ventricle which pumps the blood through the pulmonary arteries to the lungs.

After circulating through the lungs, the now purified blood returns to the auricle of the left side of the heart, through the pulmonary veins, thence into the left ventricle which has the task of pumping the blood out through the large artery called the aorta. From there it circulates to every part of the body, eventually returning to the right auricle for the cycle to start once more.

The contraction and relaxation of the muscles in the walls of the chambers of the heart—the "beating of the heart"—provides the pumping action, the main pumps being the ventricles.

By means of the heart-lung machine the blood is circulated to all parts of the body but by-passes the heart and lungs; this artificially-maintained circulation is often called the "by-pass." A tube is inserted into the *venae cavae* just at the point where they enter the heart and another into a large artery leaving the heart.

Clamps are placed across the arteries and veins entering and leaving the heart, and the other ends of the tubes are connected to the machine. The circulation to heart and lungs is thus cut off, and the pump of the machine maintains the circulation to the rest of the body, doing as well the work of the lungs by extracting carbon dioxide and adding oxygen to the blood.

The by-pass machine also enables the doctors to cool the body. Colder tissues require less oxygen to maintain their life. So cooling increases the margin of safety. As the blood passes through the apparatus a heat exchange system reduces its temperature, and the patient's body is cooled by the circulation of the colder blood.

The surgeons were now ready to start the operation to remove my heart. At this stage Clive Haupt was close to death in the adjoining theater. Indeed, he would already have died were it not for the fact that his breathing was maintained by the apparatus pumping oxygen into his lungs; breathing soon stops when the brain is severely damaged, as his had been, in which case the heart would also cease beating in a minute or two for lack of oxygen. Enough oxygen was provided for his heart to maintain its beat.

When the surgeons began the operation on me, Clive Haupt was already dead, the heart beat being maintained only by artificial means. But the doctors knew the flicker

93

of life that remained could not be sustained much longer. When the heart finally ceased to beat, it would have to be transplanted with as little delay as possible; otherwise its tissue would quickly degenerate. And if the delay were prolonged, it would not be able to resume its function when placed in its new host. I, the recipient, had, therefore, to be made ready to "take" the new heart as soon as the critical moment arrived.

The gowned and masked surgeon, one of many similarly clad in the theater, took the scalpel in his gloved hand and made a long cut from an inch or two below my Adam's apple to just above my navel. The skin edges were separated, the underlying muscles gently pulled apart, and the breast bone was exposed.

Using a special kind of band saw, he sawed through the bone from top to bottom and, with the use of hooked and curved retractors, he pulled apart the two halves of the chest cage. There were the two lungs, and the heart was seen beating inside its membranous sac, the pericardium.

Professor Barnard opened the pericardial sac and the heart, with its chambers and huge arteries and veins, was finally exposed. My breathing, at this stage, was maintained by gasses from the anesthetic apparatus by way of the tube in my wind pipe. He could now make a final and careful examination of my heart. It confirmed what he already knew. It was in such poor condition that only transplantation could possibly have saved me.

He placed cotton tapes round the aorta, the large vessel receiving the blood pumped from the left ventricle, and round the other large vessels entering and leaving the heart. These tapes would make it easier to manipulate the large vessels when the time arrived to disconnect them from the heart.

The plastic tubes from the heart lung machine were placed in position, one at the point where the *venae carvae* vessels entered the heart and the other in the large artery of the thigh. All was now ready for the removal of my heart when the by-pass machine would take over the work being done by heart and lungs.

At about this time Clive Haupt was certified dead. His breathing had stopped entirely and his heart had not only ceased beating, but the electrocardiograph indicated all life impulses in the muscles of the heart had come to an end. The electrocardiograph is a machine connected to the patient's body; it registers the electrical activity taking place in the muscles of the heart. Only when the dials showed the life processes in the heart had ceased for more than five minutes was he certified dead.

Speed was now essential to ensure that the heart, which had stopped beating, did not degenerate to a stage where it would be unable to resume activity when placed in the breast of its new host. The chest was rapidly opened, the tubes of another heart-lung machine placed at the points where blood entered and left the heart, the big blood vessels were cut through, and all structures holding the heart in place disconnected.

The heart was perfused with blood from the heart-lung machine—blood that had been cooled so that the temperature of the heart dropped from the normal 98.6 degrees Fahrenheit to about 57 degrees. The circulation to the rest of the dead body was cut off entirely. The donor heart was lifted from the chest and placed in a bowl of Ringer's solution, a special fluid containing nutrient salts, almost identical with fluids that pervade the tissues during life. The bowl of fluid was cold, its temperature only 18 degrees above the freezing point.

So rapidly had the surgeon worked that excision of the

donor heart had taken a mere two minutes, in spite of the care necessary not to damage the tissues that would have to function when connected to the new host.

The donor heart, in its bowl of fluid, was carried into the theater where I lay, with all in readiness for the excision of my own heart. The isolated heart was connected with another heart-lung machine of smaller capacity which continued to perfuse it with cold, life-sustaining blood.

Now the surgeon placed clamps across the veins and arteries of my heart. The by-pass machine was put into operation, breathing for me, and circulating cool and purified blood throughout my body with the exception of heart and lungs. My body was cooled to about 70 degrees.

Professor Barnard cut through all the blood vessels and ligaments holding my heart in position and lifted it from the site it had occupied throughout my fifty-eight years of life. The gaping void in the breast of a living man, from whom the heart had been removed, had a startling effect even on the steel-nerved workers in the theater; it was only the second time a man had lived without a heart beating in his breast.

Professor Barnard did not remove the entire heart. He left in place those parts of the walls of the auricles where the blood vessels entered. A "stump" of the heart remained.

The new heart was removed from the bowl and placed in the cavity. Small sections were removed from the walls of its auricles to fit the stumps remaining in my chest; the two were carefully trimmed and fitted, then stitched together. My new heart was now already connected to the *venae cavae* and to the veins bringing blood from my lungs. The cut ends of the other great blood vessels were painstakingly joined.

My new heart was now in place. All that needed to be done was to remove the clamps that had been placed across the great blood vessels so that my blood, instead of going to the heart-lung machine, would enter the donor heart.

This was "The Moment." The new heart had begun to function, to take the entire load of my circulation and pump the blood throughout my body. Would it spring to renewed life? It did. As it filled with blood, it immediately began to beat. It did not need the stimulation the surgeons were ready to provide by passing an electric current through the heart muscles.

The fibers of heart muscle, unlike the muscles that move our limbs—which contract only in response to messages traveling along the nerves from the brain—have an inherent, built-in, capacity to contract. As my new heart swelled with blood, this inherent quality caused it to spring to life, and soon it was beating strongly. There was no longer need for the heart-lung machine. The warmth of my own circulation soon brought my new heart to the normal temperature of the body.

Stitching blood vessels together requires a complicated, delicate, and highly-specialized technique using silken threads. To begin with, the vessels must be cut across with skill and care so that the cut ends are not unduly damaged, permitting accurate and leak-proof joining. The delicate internal linings of the vessels must remain smooth and intact as clots will form on damaged internal surfaces. To minimize the likelihood of clotting, the circulation is "heparinized." A substance called heparin, which prevents clotting, is added to the blood circulating through the body.

The trimming of the newly-transplanted heart requires the utmost care so that it will fit accurately on to the stump of tissue left behind from the removed heart.

Stitching of these into place poses problems no less difficult, or more so, than those involved in joining the cut ends of blood vessels.

All this was successfully completed, and the surgeons could see that the transplanted heart was beating strongly and successfully sustaining the circulation of its new host.

Yet even now, the operation was not at an end. The pericardial sac had to be carefully repaired to cover the new heart. The two sides of the chest cage had to be brought together, the breast bone repaired, muscles and skin carefully stitched.

Eventually, after many hours, the long process was completed, one that required not only the knowledge and techniques resulting from years of research and practice but also split-second timing in a situation for which no rehearsals had been possible.

I was wheeled from the theater with the tube still in my wind pipe to assist my breathing if necessary and a variety of tubes in the veins of my arms to sustain my life processes, providing nourishment for the anxious days that lay ahead.

Still, the first phase of the battle had been won, the first objectives achieved. Phase two of the battle was now to begin, perhaps the most dangerous phase, in which the doctors would be moving in seas uncharted amid perils unknown.

Two perils lay ahead—rejection and infection, each lying like a Scylla and Charybdis on either side of a narrow and thorny path.

The first, immediate, job was to suppress the immunological process. A foreign protein, a large, living, active mass of it, had been introduced into my system. The body would inevitably summon its resources to repel what it would consider at this stage to be a threatening invader. The lymphocytes, the musket-bearers in the body's battle against foreign protein, would soon be gathering to do their duty.

This battle can be won though not yet with certainty. The immunological processes can be suppressed with comparative ease. But here lies a snag. If the process is suppressed to too great an extent, the body is defenseless against the wide variety of germs that pervade the world we live in, that teem in the air we breathe, and the patient might succumb to even a mild infection as happened to Louis Washkansky on whom the transplant operation was successful and in whom the immunological process was effectively suppressed.

The cortico-steroids—cortisone—are the chief weapons against the rejection process. They are hormones produced by the adrenal glands, a small gland perched on the upper pole of each kidney.

These hormones have many roles but their main action is to play a part in helping the body to react to stresses of all sorts, preventing it from harming itself by its own reactions. The allergic reaction is a typical example. They also influence the functions of the tissues and organs that form lymphocytes and antibodies. They tend to slow down the rate of this production.

The large doses of cortico-steroids I was given subsequently, however, made me helplessly inadequate to deal with attack by germs, even those that would be harmless to an individual in normal health.

The picture would be further complicated by the fact that signs of rejection and infection are, in many ways, similar. It can be difficult to say which of them is taking place. Both cause a rise in temperature. Both cause an increase in the number of leucocytes in the bloodstream.

Both lead to a falling-off in function of the transplanted organ.

When faced with these signs, the doctors would have to decide rapidly which of the two processes was taking place as the treatment of the one is very different from the other.

6

SEALED OFF

I recall nothing of the four days following the operation. They were, apparently, a period af amnesia during which I spoke though I can recollect none of my words today. The nursing sisters, however, told me subsequently that soon after my return to the special suite prepared for me, I was already awake and joking.

For some reason or other I remarked to Professor Schrire: "Give my love to Eileen and tell her not to get up to her old tricks." What tricks, I ask myself today. Perhaps concealing from me what the doctors told her.

I have no memory, either, of being in an oxygen tent or of my first physiotherapy session with Miss Marilyn Sternweiler in the form of breathing exercises.

It was only on the fifth day, when I began to "register" and take note of my surroundings, that I realized I was alive. You might have expected me to say something dramatic after an epoch-making achievement that had given me back my life. Yet if one of the famous phrases of history is to be accurately attributed to me, it must be simply: "I'm alive. I can breathe now without difficulty or coughing."

I am not an imaginative or demonstrative person and, above all, I am a fatalist. I had been prepared for death. However, I must admit to a glow of satisfaction as I lay in my high surgical bed with people of flesh and blood about me. I, too, was still of the flesh and blood world.

I heard a soft voice. "How are you feeling, Dr. Blaiberg?"

"I'm fine, thanks," I whispered back. I began to take note of my physical condition. I felt little pain from the incision in my chest. A hernia operation I had undergone some years before gave me more pain and discomfort.

What, I have been repeatedly asked, did I think at the time, and since, of the eerie fact that I now had a new, a dead man's, heart, in my body. Was it strange? Do I feel differently? Has there been a change in my emotions, personality and outlook? Have I experienced any Jekyll and Hyde impulses?

My reply is that at no time have I experienced strangeness or eerieness. I am the same Philip Blaiberg who existed before the transplant, with the same emotions, feelings, and reactions I have always possessed. I always had, and I retain, my sense of humor. I still enjoy a joke, a good laugh, and my beer. Occasionally I am irritated and irritable. I love my wife and daughter as much as ever I did. I cherish my friends and life-long friendships; but I have, I think, a greater appreciation of the joy of life and living without suffering.

With strict regard for the truth, and from personal experience, I have also to report that there are no black or golden hearts, or light or stony ones. They are muscular pumps, some stronger than others, no matter how the poets describe them. And while I am about it, let me renounce, again, here, and now, any claim to heroism. I did not regard myself as a hero when I told Professor Barnard that I was willing to undergo a transplant operation; nor was I offering myself as a sacrifice for the advancement of medical science. I realized that a new

104

heart was my only chance of survival. And I took it.

I have accepted the fact that my stricken heart was removed as though it were an inflamed appendix or a hernia. The new one is carrying on the functions of the old though, of course, far better and more vigorously. I know, however, that there is still a big hurdle to surmount. I have to face the possibility of the rejection of my donor heart. There has been, as yet, no sign of it, and I face the future with the same philosophy and fatalism as I did the outcome of the operation itself.

Journalists and provocative letter-writers have tried to draw me out on my attitude toward politics, religion, and race problems. I have resolutely refused to discuss them. During my dental practice of thirty-four years I avoided controversial discussion like the plague. Business and controversy, in my opinion, don't mix. My attitude toward mankind is one of universal brotherhood.

Judging by the letters I have received from all over the world, conveying messages of goodwill from people of all creeds and beliefs, I know there is abroad a great deal of what I might call the "Christmas spirit," of peace and good will to all men. Unfortunately, people have short memories. Good will soon wanes. In my case I will endeavor to maintain it. If I succeed, even to a small degree, I will feel adequately rewarded.

For Eileen, those early days after the operation were strenuous, worrying, and filled with emotion. She telephoned the hospital each half-hour for bulletins on my condition and progress. The doctors were elated and optimistic, but she was aware of the dangers ahead, that it would be some time before I overcame them. Cables, telegrams, and the inevitable transocean telephone calls and letters swamped her. Once again she was besieged by TV and radio men and the world's leading feature writers all seeking exclusive stories. She spent hours at the telephone, nerves at breaking point.

When she learned that Clive Haupt was the donor, that his mother and young wife had agreed to the transplant, she offered them her sincere and profound gratitude for their humanitarian act. She was at Clive's funeral which, she says, was a moving and unforgettable occasion attended by twenty thousand people. She was touched by the warmth of her reception by the Colored community, who wished me well. I add my own tribute to those two women who, in the throes of grief at losing a dear one, could still feel for others. To them I owe my life.

My special isolated, air-conditioned suite in the new Ear, Nose, and Throat wing was as germ-free as possible to protect me from infection. People normally live in a bacteria-filled environment throughout their lives, but their bodies are able to cope with these bacteria. However, because of my immuno-suppressive therapy, my natural resistance had been lowered; and, for that reason, my environment had to be as bacteriologically "clean" as possible.

Eileen herself did not realize how inaccessible I was until she visited me on the fifth day. She was met by a member of the Security force and had to identify herself. At the other end of a passage was a second Security guard on the alert for reporters and others who might try to gain unauthorized entry.

She was supplied with sterilized boots, a mask, a surgical cap, into which she tucked her hair, and led to a room where she scrubbed her hands and arms in two different disinfectant solutions. Next, she was provided with a sterilized gown and rubber gloves and, as she says, "shivering with excitement," escorted to a passage where she could peek at me through a glass panel in the door. We were both so overcome that, for some moments, we could barely talk. On subsequent occasions, before I was allowed up, my bed was wheeled to the glass partition and we were able to chat comfortably through an intercom system.

My suite, originally planned as a theater, was modified by Dr. A. A. Forder, the hospital bacteriologist, to create and maintain an area as near sterile as possible. Containing four rooms, it came to be known as the "transplant unit." Between two ear-nose-and throat clinics, it was linked by a passage which was closed to the public; and even doctors not on essential business were refused admission.

Within the suite was a second passage, running parallel to the main one, which acted as a buffer zone. Medical staff who entered the suite left their coats and other outer clothes in this "buffer zone" and passed into a room where they donned sterile disposable paper caps, masks, and canvas overshoes.

The next stage was entry into a second room where they scrubbed as for a surgical operation and then put on sterile gowns and gloves. Next they passed through a swinging door into the sterilizing zone where the autoclave was installed and then, through a second swinging door, into my ward proper.

Off it opened a smaller room containing various items of equipment. The walls and ceilings of the entire suite were painted a refreshing snow white with green tiles rising to a height of about five feet from the thick plastic covered floor. It was furnished with a surgical bed, chair, adjustable stainless steel bed table, electric wall clock, and three washbasins along one wall. There

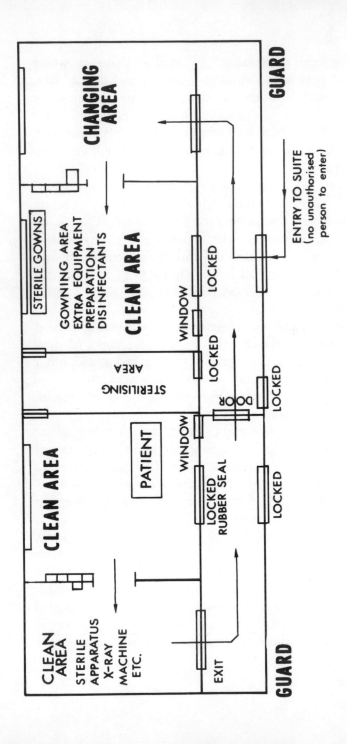

Diagram showing the unit where Dr. Blaiberg received intensive post-operative care.
The arrows indicate the direction the medical staff took when passing through the rooms.

were also a portable radio, a bath scale and, suspended above my bed, the microphone of an intercommunication apparatus. Through it I could speak to personnel in the adjoining "buffer" corridor and others in the doctors' room.

Every item of furniture and equipment had been thoroughly sterilized, or suitably cleaned, before installation. Nevertheless these, as well as the floors, beds, and walls were washed down with an antiseptic solution every four hours. The windows of the suite were opaque and those of the adjoining room, where a portable X-ray machine was housed and into which I was not allowed for a considerable time, were of clear glass.

Traffic was strictly one way. Once anyone entered, he could leave only by way of the doorless opening of my suite into the adjoining room from where he would pass through another door into the "buffer zone" and so back to the staff area. If, or when, re-entry was necessary, the entire sterilizing process had to be repeated.

My food was prepared by the dietitian in a pressure cooker in the hospital kitchens and brought, sealed, to the suite where it was warmed in a special oven in the "clean" area.

The air, walls, and equipment were constantly tested for the presence of pathogenic bacteria. Swabs were taken for biological culture to insure that relative sterility was being maintained. For some weeks I was permitted only sterile, distilled, instead of tap, water. Those who have endured distilled water even for a short time will, I know, sympathize with me.

So, for more than two months my world was peopled by masked and fully-gowned figures. Of all my visitors, I regarded Eileen as the most welcome and the best tonic. I could always see, by her eyes, that she wore a sweet and encouraging smile behind her mask. I prized it. It made by day far more, I must confess, than the eminent surgeons and scientists from foreign lands to whom I was not a husband or father, but rather a curiosity or rare medical specimen to be observed and lectured on in the hospitals and universities of the world.

I often pleaded with Eileen to spend her Sundays with her friends at the beach. She would not hear of it. Not a single day did she miss until I left the hospital.

One day she arrived with Jill who was flown from Israel to Cape Town by an American broadcasting company. Determined to give my best performance, I walked slowly and firmly as I could to the window and sat down. I looked longingly at her. She was as lovely as ever. I wore my best smile and told her I was improving by the day.

We spoke of Israel, of her life on a kibbutz and an ulpan, where she was studying Hebrew, of the spirit of the Israelis after the Six Day War. Then I saw her eyes fill with tears. So did mine; but they were tears of joy and gladness. Neither of us believed we would be spared to meet again. She paid me other visits too. Each moment was precious. The world, I felt, had nothing more to offer than the love and devotion of a wife and daughter.

During the early days of my long battle back along the road to health, I could do nothing for myself. I was as helpless as a baby. I had to be fed by spoon, even turned over in bed. But no new-born babe had a more devoted mother than I in my nurses. There were Georgie Hall, an outstanding and unpretentious personality, pretty Inge-Marie Papendieck, who was trained in Germany, vivacious brunette Liz De Villiers, petite Nurse M. E. Joubert, soft-spoken Desiree Lindsay and tall, blond Nurse V. C. Bode.

Photo by *The Cape Argus*

Mrs. Blaiberg and daughter Jill after a visit
to Dr. Blaiberg during the first month after
his operation, January 1968.

Weak though I was, there could be no delay in my physical build-up. Miss Sternweiler, my physiotherapist for most of the time (succeeded later by Miss Serina Strydom) worked ceaselessly to instruct and help me with breathing exercises, graduating to leg exercises as well. There had been a good deal of muscle waste in my legs, which were almost as thin as match sticks and as wobbly.

At first there were three sessions a day, the last as late as midnight. Neither of us complained. This was something, we knew, that had to be done no matter what the hour or the inconvenience. And, realizing how important physiotherapy is in a patient's recuperation, I always tried my utmost to do even more than was required of me. The effort was great, often exhausting, but it paid dividends.

To those who have to undergo similar treatment I would say: "Remember, by working hard at your physiotherapy sessions, you do no one any favors but yourself. They will hasten your recovery and discharge from the hospital."

Originally, there were half-hourly observations by the nurses who took my blood pressure and temperature. These gradually tapered off to hourly, then two-hourly and, finally, four-hourly intervals. I was given innumerable tablets, some at four-hourly, others at six-hourly intervals until I felt like a "pill box" with the cortisone, immuno-suppressives, Vitamin B compounds, pure Vitamin C, diuretics and antacids in liquid form I had to swallow. There was little uninterrupted sleep for me by day or night, but I was surprised how quickly I adjusted and accustomed myself to the routine.

In the early days, after the operation, Professor Barnard described my psychological condition as a "little euphoric." I was amused to hear, later, of his remark to reporters that, after being a dying man with bodily functions deteriorating, I was "brighter and more cheerful." The cortisone had given me a feeling of well-being and, in this condition, everything in the world was wonderful to me. Why shouldn't it have been? I was alive, death was so close and, it seemed, inevitable.

While I was unable to lift my arms, I was shaved and washed at about seven o'clock in the morning. Four doctors would then arrive to examine me, and a quantity of my blood was taken for laboratory tests. Swabs of my ears, throat, nose, and groin were used for bacteriological culture investigation to check for infection. Records and charts were kept and constantly studied. My circulation, blood pressure, and pulse all stood up well, and my heart was functioning adequately. My lungs were clear, and though I was tired and often slept a great deal I was more mentally alert than I had been before.

Perhaps it was too much to hope that there would be no setbacks, no moments of anxiety. One day I developed a sore throat. After each mouthful of food I had to sip water to soothe the burning when I swallowed. It caused me acute discomfort and the doctors a good deal of concern. I had no temperature, but they took no chances. They watched me day and night, checked and rechecked on their tests and the dosage of my drugs. The condition, however, responded to antifungal antibiotics and antiseptic mouth washes and, after a few days, completely disappeared.

I doubt whether any doctors have been more relieved to see a patient rid of a sore throat.

On another occasion a blood test appeared to indicate the possibility of a slight rejection of my new heart, but subsequent tests showed no sign of it and that there had been no cause for alarm. The immuno-suppressives had proved effective.

Dutifully I followed the daily routine mapped out for me. After breakfast of fruit juices, or prunes, a cereal, a couple of boiled eggs, bread and jam, cheese, and a cup of milk, Miss Sternweiler took over and I did my exercises. They were followed by the daily electro-cardiograph recording by Mr. L. W. Piller, a senior technician. It was then about 10:30 a.m., time for Eileen's daily visit and our chat through the intercom.

I usually managed to snatch some sleep before lunch, which was at about midday, and then piled heartily into my meat and vegetables, sweets and milk. The blinds were then drawn, the room darkened, and I slept until about three o'clock when I had my afternoon snack of biscuits and cheese and milk. This was followed, as I became a little stronger, by a slow walk round the room, first aided, then alone until I managed the incredible feat of circling the room five to ten times. Then, well satisfied, back I went to bed.

At about four o'clock I snoozed for an hour, and later, when I took a greater interest in affairs, I would read for an hour from five o'clock. It often happened, though, that I fell asleep immediately after my snack till 5:30 p.m. when I enjoyed the *pièce de résistance* of my day, a beer shandy that later gave way to pure beer.

One American TV technician, whom I came to know, had never heard of a shandy, much less tasted one. I instructed him how to dilute beer with lemonade in greater or lesser proportions. His face was a study, but he tried it, found it refreshing, and carried the recipe back home with him to the United States where, I believe, there are now quite a number of shandy drinkers.

Before dinner I would set out on another walk, at first aided but later by myself, and then was ready for my meal of fish and/or meat, vegtables, sweets, fruit, and milk. Again I ate voraciously.

At ten o'clock I was ready for a further snack, my back was washed and rubbed down with an anti-bedsore ointment, and I was allowed to sleep until midnight when I was awakened for another glass of milk, the usual tablets, and observations. The procedure was repeated at 2 a.m., 4 a.m. and 6 a.m. Soon it was time for my morning shave and wash and the routine of another day.

On the eighteenth day after the operation I sensed a tension in the atmosphere. Louis Washkansky had died after that period with his transplantd heart. But I can truthfully say I was feeling so much better by then that I had no thought, or fear, of rejection or a setback. Instead, I spoke of plans to hold a champagne party for the doctors and nurses to celebrate my discharge from the hospital. We waited a long time but we had it! And, for good measure, that eighteenth day, I had a lunch of pumpkin, carrots, beans, potatoes, mutton and chicken, jelly, custard, and canned fruit.

The passing of what was called the "historic" milestone gave the newspapers, television, and radio their biggest story of the day. I had become the only and longest-lived heart transplant patient and, in medical parlance, was "continuing to show good progress." But what cheered me, even more than my so-called history-making achievement, was the charming verse Inge-Marie

Papendieck composed in my honor. She was, perhaps, a little too generous in praise of her patient but I will always cherish her lines.

> And now the eighteenth day
> Dr. Blaiberg is quite gay,
> He is doing breathing exercises,
> Even without advice.
>
> A perfect patient, as we see,
> Lifting up and down the knee.
> Weisenhof we call the place here,
> Because he loves to drink his beer.
>
> One glass for the night before his sleep,
> The other one for tomorrow in the 'fridge we keep;
> That is life again, that is fun.
> Already through the room we run
> Just slowly but with open eyes,
> Chest out, head up, isn't it wonderful how he tries?
>
> Coughing still, of course, a bit
> But otherwise quite fit.
> His shiny eyes, unshaven face,
> Oh, how much we love this place.
> He dreams now of the open air
> In the sunshine in the rocking chair,
> The sea he loves by sun and moon.
> Let's pray for him it shall be soon.

I felt my luck was in. January 20, 1968 was the day of Cape Town's premier horse race, the Metropolitan Handicap, and I told Eileen to have a flutter on any horse of her fancy. I was wearing blue pajamas which matched my eyes. Among the runners were Blue Tavanier and Blue Marlin. Blue Tavanier was her choice. A reporter backed it for us on the totalisator. It ran fourth. We got our money (R2) back with a profit of 80¢.

I thought this such a good augury that I told Eileen to keep my car licensed and fully insured. If our horse could gain a place, I felt sure I would one day take my place behind the steering wheel again. I did.

I was now putting on muscle, as a result of my exercises, and the midnight physiotherapy sessions were no longer necessary. Still I was not satisfied. I wanted to do better. How much longer could I continue with the breathing exercises I was required to do? How much higher could I lift a hand or leg? I set myself targets in my recuperative activities for comparison each Saturday. Usually, I reached them by the Thursday or Friday and shared the joy of the nurses.

For some while I had had to be assisted out of my chair after meals when I ate at the table. I strove to make the pull on the nurses less and less until I could raise myself from the chair unaided. What an achievement that was! It made news. "Have you heard Dr. Blaiberg can now haul himself out of his chair without support?"

A week after the Metropolitan Handicap I passed another milestone. I washed and shaved myself, pulled on my shoes and socks for the first time, climbed out of bed, unaided, and walked twice round the ward. How many of you, who read these lines, have scented victory in the achievement of slipping on your shoes and socks? Yet what a victory it was for me! I celebrated it with my biggest breakfast in years.

It is these little things that mean so much to you in

the hospital. People have asked me what I thought about during the long weeks I spent in my suite while the world followed reports of my progress and wondered whether, or when, I would leave—to spend the rest of my life as an invalid or a vegetable. You might be surprised to know how ordinary and mundane my thoughts really were.

I did not dwell on the prospect of making a living, or the state of the world, as I read or heard about it over the radio. I thought with pleasure of the impact Professor Barnard had made in the field of science and hoped my operation would lead him to further triumphs. Otherwise, I thought mainly of those little things that so many take for granted but which make up the pattern of daily life.

I would be able to smell flowers and the sea air again. I would see buses speeding along the highways past my apartment. I would hear the siren of the electric trains as they carried commuters to work in the city. I would call "Hullo" to my friends in the street, listen again to the amusing banter of the fruit hawkers, see a good drama at the movies. Those were the things I thought of and promised myself in the days to come.

Of course, I thought often of Jill too. I had never believed I might live to see her marry, to lead her into the synagogue, perhaps one day to have grandchildren on my knee. When Eileen visited me we discussed the usual domestic matters between husband and wife. I doubt whether a recording of most of our conversations would have provided even the most news-hungry newspapers with much copy.

Eileen is a keen and shrewd observer. Nothing much escapes her. Though she did not know all that was happening behind the scenes during my seventy-four days

118

in the transplant unit, she certainly kept her eyes and ears open.

We have often spoken since of her role as onlooker on the other side of the glass partition, of what she did not tell me as the days and weeks passed, many of them far more anxious and strenuous for her than for me.

Apart from her daily visits—timed for 10:30 a.m. though she had sometimes to wait for a considerable while to be fitted into the hospital routine—she had to maintain our home, act as housewife, answer endless telephone calls and letters, give interviews to reporters, magazine writers, and radio men from all parts of the world, and entertain a constant stream of callers.

Before I go on with my side of the story and all that lay ahead, let her give some of her recollections of "Those Seventy-four Days."

"On most of my visits to Groote Schuur, in a car with special driver placed at my disposal for three months, I thought I noticed an improvement in Phil. Sometimes it was slight, but the doctors confirmed, from their charts and records, that his progress was continual and my spirits rose. I could smile a genuine smile—I knew he could 'see' it even behind my surgical mask—and I did not have to force one as I had for so many months.

"My visits seemed to stimulate him, and as I sat chatting through the intercom and watched the attention given him by the doctors and nurses I was filled with gratitude. They far exceeded the bounds of duty.

"Even in the early days when he was so weak he had a quip for me, the doctors, nurses, everyone. He told me with pride how his breathing was improving all the time as a result of his exercises and how his legs were responding to treatment. 'Eileen,' he said one day, 'you can't believe what it means to be able to breathe again without suffering.'

"During all the time he spent in his suite, I don't remember a word of complaint from him. I was surprised one day, about two weeks after the operation, when he said, 'Oh, how wonderful it is to be without pain.'

" 'What do you mean?' I asked. 'You've never complained about pain before.'

" 'Well, naturally, the wound down my chest was a bit uncomfortable, and I found it difficult to turn in my bed. But,' he added with a smile, 'it's gone now.'

"That was typical of him. He always declared he had no pain or discomfort until it was over so that I would not worry after I left him.

"I learned to have more respect for him on those daily visits than in all our years together. I realized what a stoical and uncomplaining husband I had. The doctors and nurses agreed he was an ideal patient in every way. They were sure his progress was also largely due to his unconcern about his own suffering and his spirit of determination to get well and over every hurdle as he reached it. The most menial member of the staff found him jolly and full of fun and he tried to make the duties of the nurses as pleasant as possible. It was most unusual, they told me, to find this consideration in a patient as ill as Phil.

"One day, I remember, during Jill's visit, he said he had a 'big surprise' for us.

" 'I want you to watch very carefully,' he said. 'I'm going to walk for you. *That'll* show you!'

"It was a pathetic sight as we saw him lean on two nurses and take a few faltering steps with a smile of happiness on his face. Afterward I believe, he asked a nurse whether he had put on a good performance. If he had only known how Jill and I sobbed after we left. We could not control our tears. He had such pride in his 'big surprise.' It made us feel humble that such a little achievement could have meant so much to him.

"A few weeks later, after Jill had returned to Israel, he told me he had fixed a little mirror to the wall and shaved himself without the aid of the nurses. That was another 'milestone,' as he called it, along the road to recovery. It was such a small thing, but it again gave him such happiness. It showed Progress, he said, with a capital P.

"Though Phil made light of his sore throat it was, while it lasted, a nightmare to me and the entire transplant unit. Our nerves were on edge. I telephoned the doctors constantly, every hour, to inquire about him. I could not sleep at night thinking of the possible causes and the grim implications. At the back of our minds, I suppose, was the fear of an infection that might have fatal consequences.

"I can talk about it calmly now, but I will never forget my anxiety and downright pessimism then. Sometimes I thought it the beginning of the end. Had Phil come so far, undergone a successful transplant operation, only to. . . . I tried to stop my thoughts at that point. After my restless nights, however, there was Phil waiting for me, his usual, bright self, wearing his jolly smile.

" 'How is your throat?'

" 'It's all right,' he said. 'It's nothing. There's nothing to worry about. Just a little irritation. It'll go away. You'll see.'

"I played along with him. I pretended I also believed it was not serious. I would not allow him, for a moment, to guess my thoughts. I believe he thought he had convinced me that there was 'nothing to it,' nothing, really, to concern myself about.

"But the doctors could not pretend. They suffered as I did. Some of them, too, had sleepless nights. The slightest abnormality in Phil, a point up in his temperature, an ache or pain he had not known the day before—all were of the greatest concern to them.

"They admitted they had nothing to guide them. At that time Phil was the only living man with a transplanted heart. Who knew what problems might suddenly, and unexpectedly, arise, in spite of all the drugs and treatment given him? There were always the imponderables, the unpredictables.

"Whether the doctors told me or not, I somehow knew, probably by intuition, when things were not going well or as well as they hoped. Sometimes I drove away from the hospital in a state of nerves and tension, leaving behind a husband who did not seem to have a care in the world, who said good-by to me with a smile and a jest. But I always sensed when the doctors were worried. Looking back on those days I am forever thankful that our fears were false alarms as Phil said they were. If only I had been able to show his courage and optimism, how much less I would have suffered.

"Not a day passed without reporters waiting for me. Their questions were endless. What had Phil said or done that day? What had we spoken about? He was now one of the main sources of world news, and his words seemed to be as important, to the newspapers and broadcasting companies and televiewers at any rate, as any uttered by a president or prime minister. I know that sounds a bit dramatic—but there it was. What scrap of news had I

122

to tell them? Sometimes I was at my wits' ends to satisfy their curiosity.

"Phil was amused one day when I said to him, 'Please, darling, say something funny.' He looked at me as though I were crazy.

" 'Funny? What for?'

" 'For the reporters,' I said. I told him I simply didn't know what to tell them any longer except that he was improving and still enjoying his food.

" 'Well,' he grinned, 'why not tell them to jump in the lake?'

"That's all very well,' I said. 'But you haven't got to face their grilling every time I put my face outside the hospital door.'

"The reporters certainly had their problems. Their editors wanted something different each day, something they could headline. What appeared to be rather stupid questions to me were put, it seemed, in all earnestness. But, I was told, it was 'an angle.'

"One reporter suggested that I ask Phil when he would climb Lion's Head again. I did.

" 'What does he mean—Lion's Head?' Phil retorted. 'It won't be long before I'll be climbing Devil's Peak. It's higher and more of a challenge.'

"Even that news item, I believe, was cabled round the world as an example of Phil's sense of humor and his hopes for the future. Descriptions and radio pictures of Lion's Head and Devil's Peak followed. Phil was certainly helping to boost South Africa as a tourist attraction.

"Then the reporters wanted details of his menus and his appetite. I told them. Next day the products of the Groote Schuur Hospital kitchens, as delivered to Phil in his suite, were quoted throughout the Continents.

123

"I learned to be absolutely accurate in every word I said. If I happened to make a remark that seemed to be incorrect, I knew there would be thousands who would certainly let me know. For months letters would arrive demanding an explanation as to why I said this-or-that.

"Once I mentioned that Phil enjoyed a hearty breakfast. This, too, became world news. A woman in Australia assumed that his 'hearty breakfast' included a plentiful helping of bacon and eggs, toast and marmalade, tea or coffee. She wrote warning him against the perils of the breakfast tray and urged him, above all, to avoid bacon. Phil never eats it.

"All the time I was being photographed wherever I went, entering and leaving the hospital, shopping, lunching, and dining. I became heartily sick of my face staring at me from the newspapers. But the photographers had their instructions and duties. I was trailed, 'shot,' and, once more, I was in the papers. Phil was highly amused. I wasn't.

" 'Now you know what kings and queens have to put up with,' he grinned.

" 'They can have it,' I said with feeling.

" 'And it's all my fault,' Phil apologized.

"The world, I found, continued to be publicity and news crazy. There was a fierce and ever-increasing competition among newspapers, magazines, radio, and television for a 'beat' on the Blaiberg Story. Even my own daily doings, many trivial, were page one news.

"Well, I decided, if that was the way it had to be, there was nothing for me but to resign myself to it.

"My attempt to avoid the deluge before Phil's operation, had landed me in a spot of bother with some newspapers. They believed I was withholding news from them because of some contract I had made, whereas the truth was simply that I desperately wanted to avoid the operation being turned into some sort of circus stunt.

"I found life much easier when I let the press have what they wanted when they wanted it. I couldn't argue with them and carry my worries and burdens at the same time. Though there were exceptions, I must add that reporters and television teams were polite, helpful, and considerate. If you are frank with them, explain your difficulties and problems, they will respect your confidences. They had a job to do and, as Phil said, we should help them all we could.

"About four weeks after the operation, some of the doctors told Phil and me that he might be allowed to go home in the near future. How thrilled we were. But the weeks dragged by and turned into months and still nothing happened. It was a strain not knowing when the Great Day would arrive. Now I was put off with 'maybe next week.' Next week came and went. Still Phil remained in his suite.

"Besides the uncertainty, which was hard enough to bear, the press now started to nag and calls came not only from South African newspapers but from all over the world for the top secret date. Some editors were convinced I knew but would not disclose it, that I had a scoop up my sleeve for some favored publication. It just wasn't true. I knew as little as they did.

"As the weeks passed, I realized that my life and the world I had known were changing. I was dined and wined by journalists and V.I.P.'s until I think I knew the menus of every restaurant and hotel grill room in Cape Town. It became almost a standing joke that you could, or should, ask Eileen Blaiberg where to get the best meal in town.

"In this new world I gained a host of new and good

friends, many among the doctors and nurses at Groote Schuur Hospital. I took along cake for our little tea parties when I visited Phil. I made many other worthy friends in those seventy-four days, and their friendship and kindness to me and to Phil are something we continue to cherish.

"What pleased me most was that, as a result of my new status as wife of a celebrity, I was able to help publicize a number of good causes. I have been a blood donor for many years and took part in a campaign for blood on behalf of the Western Province Blood Transfusion Service which played a vital role in the operation.

"I was bled on a couch alongside the Acting State President, Mr. Tom Naude, another veteran blood donor, and we were photographed together. That was *one* photograph I welcomed. I believe the publicity increased the number of donors. The sequel for me, personally, was not particularly pleasant. When I visited Phil later I almost blacked out. I had been overtaxing myself. However, Phil suspected nothing, gave me a figurative pat on the back for my efforts, and I soon recovered.

"I had a glimpse, too, of the wonderful world of television. I gave an interview which was shown throughout the world, and along came shoals of mail wishing Phil well. Jill, too, was televised in Israel and I soon had letters about my 'beautiful daughter.'

"It seems strange that though millions of televiewers have seen and heard Phil and me, we have yet to see ourselves as others saw us. Perhaps, one day, before these films pass into the archives we will be able to relive those days in some television studio in the United States or Britain or Japan. We have no television yet in South Africa."

126

One day Miss Sternweiler brought a two-step "staircase" to the suite. I was to try to mount it. This was my Everest. At first it was an exhausting effort and beyond my strength to climb even the first rung unaided. Eventually I succeeded. *That* was really something. I had developed from a walker to a climber.

But I had to learn to hasten slowly. Once I almost tumbled off the staircase. Fortunately, Miss Sternweiler and a nurse held on to me and prevented a fall. Still I went on trying. At last came victory. I conquered the second step as well. Now I stood on top of my little world. No mountaineer, at the pinnacle of a perilous climb, was prouder than I.

Will I ever forget that day in February, 1968, forty-three days after the operation, when I faced the hospital official photographer. I was in my pajamas, shaving. But that was how the world was to see me for the first time. The photographer had to undergo the entire sterilization process before being allowed to approach the glass partition and take his pictures through an eye-level glass panel above the door leading into my suite. The angle was awkward, but he did his best.

Newspapers all over the world featured the picture on their front pages—and speculated when, or whether, I would leave Groote Schuur. The caption in one London newspaper referred to me as "Forty-four Days Old." But Eileen was horrified. She claimed that her "good-looking" husband resembled Al Capone or some other Public Enemy Number One. It didn't bother me. What if I was no Gregory Peck or Laurence Olivier? It was another handsome milestone reached and passed.

To the people of South Africa I gave a message in English and Afrikaans, through the South African Broadcasting Corporation, thanking the thousands of listeners who sent me greetings and good wishes.

Television teams flew into Cape Town from the United States and Germany to present me to the world "in person." Special sterilized lighting apparatus was installed in my ward. I was to "star," I was told, on TV screens in millions of homes as the "Man of the Hour" or the "Man With the New Heart." I put on my best smile and endeavored, to the best of my ability, to answer questions and sing a song or two though I have no illusions about my voice. My imagination still boggles at the thought that I was seen and heard in Alaska and Alabama, in New York, London, and Paris, in Tokyo and Teheran, in Israel and Ireland.

Was I, I asked myself, regarded as a freak or Professor Barnard's guinea pig, or as a fellow human being who had the good fortune to be snatched from the brink of death by a miracle of medical science? The countless letters that reached me convinced me I was seen mainly as a symbol of hope for heart sufferers now and in the future.

Though I was, by now, used to the deluge of publicity and the interest people showed in my progress and well-being, I was often amazed at the effects. I had only to say a word or two, it seemed, or tell Eileen some tidbit about my daily doings, and they winged their way round the globe. Then someone or other would write to me or send a gift.

In my "baby stage," for instance, when I could do virtually nothing for myself, I had found great comfort in Inge-Marie Papendieck's singing at bedtime. She used to sing my favorite lullaby, Brahms' "Cradle Song," which sent me into a peaceful slumber. I liked nothing better than to close my eyes and listen to her sweet voice. Do you remember the words:

> Slumber sweetly, my dear
> For angels are near thee
> To watch over you
> The silent night through.
> When the dawn peepeth through
> God will wake them and you.

My bedtime lullaby became news in the German newspapers and on TV. Not long afterward two records of the "Cradle Song" arrived for me by air from Germany. One was a gift from a 14-year-old child accompanied by a charming letter written in excellent English. Someone else sent an ornamental musical clock. I had merely to touch a cord and the lullaby would peal out. It now hangs on the wall of my apartment among other treasures and mementoes of those days.

During my daily peregrinations round my room I had not been allowed to enter the adjoining one but, by standing at the opening, I had a view, through its clear glass windows, of the trees, the blue skies, and streaming sunlight. How wonderful the world looked, how fortunate those who strolled about without effort, taking for granted the outdoor life, the pure air in their lungs. How I would enjoy these precious privileges, I told myself, again, when the time came. I toiled even longer and harder at my exercises, set my weekly targets higher.

At last I was permitted to enter the forbidden room. Now I could stand opposite the sealed window and gaze on to the street in front of the hospital, wave to passers-by, and pose for photographs. I must have faced a thou-

For well-wishers outside the hospital,
Dr. Blaiberg makes a V for victory.

sand movie cameras and others with telephoto lenses. I took the liberty of giving the Churchill V-sign. World travelers arriving in Cape Town made special trips to Groote Schuur, during their sight-seeing, to wave to me. I was now, it seemed a tourist attraction rivaling the usual visits to the Cape Nature Reserve and the ascent, by cableway, to the summit of Table Mountain.

All the time my strength increased and my new heart beat steadily. My walking capacity improved. The wasted leg muscles were getting firmer, stronger. I found I could walk ten times around both rooms in my suite five times a day. I calculated how far that would have taken me along Adderley Street, Cape Town's main thoroughfare. The distance, perhaps, was not very impressive but no Marathon walker, I am sure, felt as I did when I achieved this latest goal.

To add to my joy, Dr. Forder relented and allowed me to drink tap water. To me it tasted like the nectar of the gods. I was permitted an intake of ten large glasses of water each twenty-four hours, not a great deal for one used to two glasses of iced water with each meal. But on my walks, as I passed the taps, I resolutely resisted the temptation for an "extra." The limit set, I knew, was for my own good.

One of the team's doctors who heard of my continued prowess as a walker came to watch my performance. I was determined to impress him. I walked and walked, proudly and as erect as I could, a big grin on my face. He nodded approval and congratulated me. To him this was of significance in my recuperation and the soundness of my new heart.

I became a trifle too overconfident and tried a little show-off-manship. Squaring up to him, as though I were in a boxing ring, I did a little light footwork. Momentarily I forgot that my spindly, indiarubber legs had not yet recovered their strength, that I was still far from fit even for shadow boxing. Down I went on the floor.

For a moment doctor and nurses were horror-struck. They believed the world's prize guinea pig had injured himself. No world disaster could have matched the consequences. They need not have worried. They helped me up. I thanked them and set off again, unaided, to traverse my little kingdom once more.

"You certainly gave me a scare," the doctor said. "I thought, for a moment, that my own heart had stopped beating." They all agreed, however, that I had gone down as gracefully and relaxed as any ballet dancer.

"It was done reflexly," I told them proudly. I went on to explain that I had been taught, by my rugby coach at school, *how* to fall. We had to relax all muscles when we were tackled. And so we never strained or pulled muscles or broke bones. Following his advice, and putting his suggestions into practical effect, I escaped injury through my rugby career except for a scratch or bruise. I had not forgotten what I learned more than forty years ago. They agreed wholeheartedly, and with relief, that it was just as well at that stage of my recovery, particularly during my interlude of shadow boxing.

Meanwhile, my appetite increased until it became almost insatiable. The scale showed I had been steadily gaining weight. Whatever I ordered was brought to me in copious quantity. I had but to express a desire for some special food, and it was tastily prepared and sent to me by the dietitian and her staff. No gourmet or gourmand was ever more pampered.

However, even perfection palls. I longed for home cooking and the favorite dishes our maid, Katie Booysen, prepared. I spoke longingly of her egg soufflé. No one, I asserted proudly, could make one like Katie. News of her qualities as a chef appeared in the Press—together with the recipe. She has many copyists now.

Though I have always been a great reader, I had shown little interest in books, magazines, or newspapers during the first few weeks in my suite. I could not concentrate. The radio news bulletins about myself sometimes gave me a laugh. They were not always as accurate as they might have been—at any rate, in my opinion. Later I began to read voraciously and listened as well to radio talks, plays, and quizzes in which I tried to pit my wits against the experts on some panel or other, and shared in the excitement of competitions with prizes of cars, washing machines, and expensive jewelry.

With no sign of rejection of my heart, the steady improvement in my bodily condition and functions, and general good spirits, the doctors were convinced I was well on the way to recovery and could expect to return home at no distant date. Eminent cardiac surgeons and specialists of all kinds from Germany, Holland, France, Spain, Iran, and Chile flew to Cape Town to visit and questions me. Among them were several who were sceptical about what they had read in the popular press and wanted to satisfy themselves of my physical existence.

Professor Barnard was a particularly welcome visitor, and his examination and study of reports on my progress invariably impressed him. When he was abroad, he telephoned the hospital regularly to inquire about me and, on his return, after an exhausting air trip of thousands of miles, he would call at Groote Schuur, though it entailed changing into sterile regalia, before going home.

There was one night I will never forget. He walked into my room, masked and dressed in his usual sterile outfit, carrying a transparent plastic box. In it was my old

133

heart in a preservative solution. Outside, behind the glass panel in the passage, was an official photographer similarly garbed, who was to record the occasion.

Professor Barnard and I sat on my bed and examined my heart with cool professional interest. He showed me that more than ninety per cent of the muscle had become fibrosed or converted into functionless scarred tissue. When Professor J. G. Thomson (Pathologist to Groote Schuur Hospital and Head of the Department of Pathology, University of Cape Town) saw it, he said that, had he not known it was removed from my chest, he would have declared it was from a corpse. How I had managed to remain alive until the transplant was a miracle in itself.

Professor Barnard looked up from my heart and said quizzically, "Dr. Blaiberg, do you realize that you are the first man, in the history of mankind, to be able to sit, as you are now, and look at his own, dead, heart?"

Believe it or not, I had been so interested, perhaps shocked, by the appearance and condition of my heart that I had not given a thought to the historic implications.

"Now that you mention it," I said somewhat abashed, "It does occur to me that I have been looking at my heart."

The photographer's bulbs flashed and the occasion was captured for posterity. The heart itself is now a celebrated pathological specimen.

Other memories of my stay in my suite come flooding back. Some are grim, of the battle that had to be ceaselessly fought and won, of times of strain and anxiety, of occasional boredom. But generally there was a spirit of conviviality.

A nurse, suggesting that one of the walls needed brightening, hung a reproduction of a painting of the

British Houses of Parliament, with the Thames and London Bridge in the foreground. I often studied it thinking of my student days and when, maybe, I would see them again.

Other nurses snipped out press photographs of Eileen and myself, sterilized them, and plastered another wall with them.

One of the medical team, who visited me, used to show his satisfaction with my condition by greeting me with bursts from "Hello, Dolly!" I joined in. All, I knew, was well. On other days he did not sing. I thought there was something on his mind. Perhaps the blood tests had not been up to the standard he expected. Next day, however, I was accorded a "Hello, Dolly!" greeting once more. All was right again.

My gray hairs often led to my being made a confidante by some of the young nurses who tended me. I found the course of true love does not run smooth anywhere. Hospitals are no exception. Professional efficiency, expert handling of medical equipment, the starched uniform, make no difference.

One day I noticed a nurse in tears. She had had a row with her boy friend. The end of the world, it seemed, had come for her. Nothing would be the same again.

"Don't take it seriously," I said to her from my ripe experience as a married man of thirty-one years' standing. "It'll blow over. All young people go through these trials. When I was a young man and engaged . . ."

I did not tell *all*, but sufficient to console her. She listened respectfully, seemingly accepted that I knew what I was talking about, and dried her tears. A day or two later she was all smiles once more. She and her boy friend had made up. The sun shone again.

To others I was an amateur "marriage counselor" or

"man-management counselor." In this capacity, I believe, I gave advice with circumspection, again based on personal experience though, I hasten to add, I am not seeking professional, or even part-time employment in this uncertain field.

As the weeks lengthened into months I became restless and anxious to leave. Life in a luxury suite, even with one's every wish and whim gratified, can become tiring and monotonous. I yearned for my sunny apartment, my home surroundings, my favorite armchair with a glass of beer at my side. I had been improving by the day. The doctors admitted it. So did the physiotherapist and the nurses. What then, I inquired, was delaying my departure?

I began to nag. Jokingly I remarked that I had already cost the hospital a mint of money and it would pay them to see the back of me. As a matter of interest, my operation entailed expenditure of about £15,000 ($36,000) though I paid only £2.10s ($6.00) a day, which included the hundreds of expensive drugs I had swallowed for nearly three months. My own bill amounted to £230 ($552) which was, however, fully covered by the hospitalization scheme of the Dental Association Professional Provident Society.

They heard me patiently. I was, indeed, fit to leave, but apparently they wanted Professor Barnard, then abroad, to accompany me out of the hospital, the first man to live with a transplanted heart. I did not want to deny him that satisfaction. It would be the culmination of his triumph, the final answer to those who criticized Dr. Barnard because heart transplants were "premature."

Professor Barnard returned. He drove, as usual, to Groote Schuur from the airport, studied the latest reports on my condition, and it was agreed that I would be discharged on Saturday, March 16. The news was to be "top secret." The authorities needed time to organize a cordon at the hospital exit, arrange an escort, mount a police guard at our apartment to ward off the inevitable curiosity-seekers, autograph hunters, and my good friends, though sometimes over-enthusiastic, the journalists.

Eileen mentioned no date to anyone, not even her closest friends, and this, she told me afterward, led to bedlam. Telephone calls came day and night from newspapers and television networks all over the world demanding to know the date of my return home. She was determined not to give it. Photographers wanted pictures of the chair I would sit in and the bed I would lie on during my convalescence. They drove her almost to distraction.

Nevertheless she vowed that no one would enter our apartment at least for two days before I returned so that it would be neat and tidy after a thorough spring-cleaning.

On March 15, the day before my discharge Eileen brought me a shirt, a pair of slacks, shoes, my Royal Dental Hospital blazer and cravat. I slept soundly and happily that last night at the hospital. Eileen, however, had a far from restful night. Again there were calls from newspapers and television teams for the exact time of my departure. Once more the "top secret" remained undisclosed.

Eileen set out for Groote Schuur early on the Saturday morning to accompany me home and, within moments, the news spread. When she reached the hospital she was so excited that she did not hear, or understand, a word the nurses told her of the home treatment she would have to undertake. She was so keyed up and trembling that she

Leaving the hospital: Dr. Blaiberg
with Professor Barnard.

Dr. and Mrs. Blaiberg in the car on
the way home from the hospital.

Dr. and Mrs. Blaiberg entering their
apartment on his return from the hospital.

could not even pack my few belongings. When she was invited into my suite, for the first time in seventy-four days, to help me dress, she stood and gaped. For the first time in her life she was speechless with joy and happiness.

Professor Barnard and the official photographer were also there. They had discarded their masks, caps and gowns. The nurses still wore their sterilized outfits.

"Why are you wearing your masks now?" Professor Barnard bantered. "Dr. Blaiberg is passing into a bacteria-filled world." Off came the masks.

For the first time I saw my nurses. I had seen their eyes before and could identify them only by their voices and vital statistics. They were prettier than I had imagined.

As I looked round the suite for the last time, I was overcome by an indescribable feeling of nostalgia. For me it had come to mean so much in care and devotion, kindliness and self-sacrifice by so many by day and night. I owed them a debt of gratitude I could never repay.

The incongruous thought suddenly occurred to me that this was my second birthday in a year. January 2, 1968, the day of the operation, was the date of the conception of my new life. The seventy-four days in the sterile suite were my second period of gestation. Now, today, March 16, I was being reborn into the world. Birthdays, I felt, called for joy and gladness and song.

I had a lump in my throat when I gave my final singing performance, my best, I hoped—"When Irish Eyes Are Smiling" (though, I confess, I had a tear in mine) and the perennial "Hello, Dolly!"

Two of the nurses, Liz De Villiers and Desiree Lindsay, responded with a song they had composed specially for me based on "Get Me to the Church on Time" from *My Fair Lady*.

140

I am going home this morning
Spruced up and looking in my prime.
The people have come to see me
To show how much they've missed me.
Get me to my home on time.

I could have hugged them.

We laughed and chatted, waiting for my time of departure. I became excited. I wondered how the fresh air, the wonderful, contaminated, bacteria-laden air would taste. I couldn't wait for the rays of the sun on my face and the caress of the wind.

At last they put me in a wheelchair, like an invalid. Quite a procession we made as I was trundled along the gleaming corridor to an elevator that was to take me down to the main entrance to the block.

I had been told the world press and television teams were waiting outside with hundreds of citizens who had gathered, hours before, to give me a rousing welcome and send-off. I had no intention of allowing the world to see Professor Barnard's patient leave the hospital in a wheelchair. No. I would use my legs. I raised myself out of the chair and walked steadily toward the door and outside. I felt elated and a new vigor seemed to flow through me as I passed over the threshold into the world I had yearned for so long.

Now I was in the air and sunshine again. I could have wept for joy. I was to live with people once more, share in the problems, the excitement of everyday existence. And it was due to the transplant team, some of whom stood smiling beside Professor Barnard and me while the crowd clapped and waved, and to the nurses so devoted and patient during my convalescence.

Nearby was Eileen, gay and laughing and proud, she

who had been so often near to tears and sometimes shed them alone. For some moments we stood, our little group, like a tableau in a play.

I can recall all the scenes and words spoken that day, but I cannot adequately describe my emotions, my innermost feelings of thankfulness, the desire to cry out: "I'm alive. I'm alive. Do *you* all know what it means to be alive?"

Around me, held back by a group of policemen, were laughing, waving people. They were, I felt, my friends. I wanted to shake each one by the hand and say "How are you, friend?" But they all wanted to know how *I* was.

I remember one young reporter perched on the shoulders of a perspiring colleague. He grinned and cried, "Hi, Doc! What's it like to breathe contaminated air again?"

"Contaminated?" I said. "It's heaven."

Hundreds of cameras were trained on me. I thought I'd give the Press photographers and television teams something different. "Shall I kiss the girls?"

"Get on with it," they shouted and prepared to "shoot." But the nurses in the immediate danger zone did not believe kissing patients in public was appropriate even on such an occasion. I hugged two of them instead.

A big shiny car waited to drive Eileen and me to our apartment in Wynberg. The crowd parted as I walked along. Traffic officers, our escort, revved up their motorcycles, and we moved off. Bystanders tapped on the windows and shouted "Good luck" and "Good health." I looked up at the scores of nurses and doctors waving to me from windows and balconies. What wonderful people, I thought, people of all races who made up the population of Cape Town. How proud I was to be one of them, that it was Cape Town's Groote Schuur Hospital where I was given a new life.

We cruised along the highway, past vistas and buildings I knew so well. There were smells I thought I would never know again. It was late summer with autumn just ahead. But the trees and the grass on the wooded slopes of Table Mountain were still green and fresh. The flowers on the traffic island in the center of the road were beginning to fade. To me they were new and a pure delight. The houses we passed looked freshly painted, the gardens around them as though they had been watered and trimmed that morning. People strolled along the pavements chatting to friends, doing their weekend shopping. They took no notice of me. One day, I promised myself, I would join them.

Then we were at Highbury. Again there were the crowds, the reporters and photographers and the police to deal with autograph hunters and others over-enthusiastic in their welcome. I didn't mind. This, to me, was living again. Then, up a few steps, with the aid of strong police hands, and into the elevator to the second floor; along a passageway, the longest distance I had walked since the operation, to the door of my apartment, number 204, at the end.

Waiting for me was Katie, our maid. She grinned hugely. I said, "Hello, Katie. I'm back." She said, "Hello, doctor, welcome home."

At long last I was home again, surrounded by my books, the ornaments Eileen and I had collected over the years, the well-loved pictures, all the inanimate, but precious, objects that go to make a home.

I was a trifle weary after the excitement, but the sense of elation remained. My life now had a future as well as a past. Automatically my thoughts turned again to Professor Barnard. This day was more of a triumph for him than for me.

He it was who had the courage to transplant a new heart in me after his first patient died. Courage shown on the spur of the moment, as in war, is admirable. But the cold, calculated courage he had shown, while the world watched him, was courage indeed. There have been other transplants since mine. The surgeons who undertook them were courageous, too, but they were following the path pioneered and mapped out by Chris Barnard and his team.

"Eileen," I said, "they are making such a fuss over me, and I can't help feeling a bit of a fraud. This is really Chris Barnard's day." The headlines, television programs, and radio broadcasts about me, and the letters and cables streaming into our apartment really belonged, I said, to him. I was a bystander, though a happy one, in his triumph.

It was lunch time. To Katie's delight I was hungry. She had been preparing all morning. But she was slightly worried too. After the special foods at the hospital, I might have different tastes.

I reassured her. "Katie, there's nothing like good home cooking—especially when you do it."

She fussed about like a cat with her kittens. Was this all right? Would I have more of this or that? Did I want something else? She need not have worried. It was the finest meal I had eaten.

I stretched out on my bed for a nap. A delightful tiredness came over me. "Eileen," I said. "The world is marvelous. Just bloody marvelous." In a few moments I was asleep.

7

LIFE WITH A NEW HEART

Life in the past months has continued to be marvelous. But after all Eileen and I have been through I think, humbly, we deserve it. Together we have discovered a new world of unending kindness, good will, generosity, and sincere friendship. We are happy in everything we do. Material things mean nothing to us.

I laugh and joke and throw care out of the window. So does Eileen. Nothing is more precious than health, and I am determined to regain mine, no matter how long it takes.

Forgivably, perhaps, I consider myself the doyen of the world's heart transplant "Club." Each time I learn of a patient receiving a new heart, I send a message of good-will and follow his progress with the fervent hope that he will recover and live as happily and contentedly as I.

Let me tell you something of what has happened to Eileen and me since the day of our homecoming, of the people we have met and the joys we have known, of the change that has come over our lives.

But first I pause, as I did on that unforgettable first day home, to think gratefully of Dorothy Haupt whose act of unselfishness meant life to me.

We had not yet met though she had seen me on Jan-

147

uary 2, 1968, after her husband died when I was wheeled past her into the operating theater. My eyes were closed. I was so ashen-faced and near death that I appeared to her to be beyond aid, even with the transplant of Clive's young heart.

I had wanted so much to meet her, tell her with my own lips of my debt of gratitude to her. Now that I was home it was still not possible to meet her face to face. I telephoned.

"But you've just come out of the hospital," she said in surprise. "I didn't expect to hear from you for some time." She had read of my progress and was as excited and happy for me as my own folks.

"I'm fit now," I told her. "I want to thank you, Dorothy, for all you've done for me."

As I write these words, they seem stiff, formal, cold. But how could I thank her adequately in words on the telephone? They just wouldn't come though emotion gripped me.

It was the same when I met Dorothy five days later. She was one of the first visitors to my apartment. Eileen answered the doorbell. We looked at one another for a moment or two without speaking. Dorothy Haupt had lost a life. I had gained one. What does one say in such circumstances? What *can* one say without giving way to tears and the sentiments we all felt but would not show.

"Hullo, Dorothy," I managed. "I'm so glad you were able to come here so that I could meet you." How terribly unimaginative I was, I told myself. But, perhaps, that is how we all wanted it. I think we had been fearful emotion would get the better of us.

Dorothy sat on a settee, and we chatted casually. We showed her some of the letters we had received from all parts of the world, many expressing admiration for her deed. She, too, had a heavy mail from sympathizers.

Katie brought in tea and cake. Dorothy remarked how well I looked. "You seem," she said, "to be in even better health than the newspaper photographs show."

I could not say the same for her. She seemed weary and dispirited. Her eyes lacked sparkle.

"You need more rest," I said. Again I was aware that my words were rather like a doctor's advice to a patient who had been overworking.

"Yes. I am tired. But I'm taking a tonic. I'm sure that will strengthen me."

I telephoned her a number of times after her visit, and later Eileen and I shared with her the happy surprises that followed her great sorrow. If she reads what I have written here, I want her to know that my poor, formal words hid an emotion and gratitude I had never known before.

You might like to glance round my apartment where I am working on this book. It is on a corner, and from my balcony I can just see the wide vista of Greater Cape Town which has a population of about a million and I, my friends are fond of telling me, unique among them. I prefer to be called the luckiest. In the far distance you can glimpse the blue waters of Table Bay, just the last dip of the bay as it curves into land before sweeping out again.

That painting of Professor Barnard in the hallway is the work of a Cape Town art teacher. Everyone admires it. The woodcut on the kist opposite was a gift from a Colored man; one head on the woodcut is of Professor Barnard, the other of me.

149

The first door on the right of the hallway leads into the dining room. Your eye will at once fall on a silver tray with an array of bottles and tubes. From them come the two dozen tablets I take each day; they used to total thirty-two, but dosages have been gradually reduced. I swallow them in batches four times daily. Most important are the immuno-suppressive drugs, which counteract my body's rejection of the new heart, and an infection-suppressive to deal with any infection that might affect me. Then there are the Vitamins B and C, the oral antiseptics and antacids.

In true army style, I take the pills from the bottles and line them up. Then I pop them into my mouth, one after the other, and down they go without a bump on the way. I keep a little notebook in which I record my pill-taking routine just in case I forget them or take them twice instead of once. Pill-taking can become such a habit that you are liable to forget five minutes afterward having taken them at all.

In the lounge, a sizable, comfortable room, my favorite chair where I write is backed by a long row of windows. Visitors who have not called before sit at a distance on a settee opposite me. It is safer that way. Not only do I get the fresh air from the open windows and the sunshine streaming in on me, but there is less danger of cross-infection.

Though life has now become, more or less, normal for me, there is still this disadvantage that distinguishes me from other patients recuperating after an operation. My doctors have insisted that I should not come into immediate close contact with strangers. Many individuals spread germs without realizing it. There are some who are, outwardly, perfectly healthy but are nonetheless carriers of disease in virulent form. The resistance of their own bodies to the germs has meant that these become more powerful and are a hazard to anyone with reduced ability to fight them.

I am such a person, not because of any inherent weakness in my body, but because of the immuno-suppressive drugs I am still taking. So I often greet newcomers with a jocular: "Keep your distance, brother. You're in the presence of the purple. Don't come too near me."

In that way I warn them that, much as I would like to shake them by the hand, or sit beside them, I dare not for the sake of my health. Occasionally I would add, "Professor Barnard took a lot of trouble over this operation. I don't want to die now of pneumonia and spoil it all for him!" I was cautious at first even with special friends, like reporters and photographers, who visited my apartment periodically, but later I felt safer. They assisted me down the stairs and I drove with them in the same car; it was obvious they were not "carriers" of germs dangerous to me. When, however, anyone had the slightest cold, a sore throat, or a sneezing bout, he stayed away or wore a surgical mask and kept his distance.

Special visitors, in close contact with me for the first time, were required to wear these masks. There were, for example, my barber, Barney Albert, who would have had difficulty in cutting my hair from a distance of eight feet, and my tailor, Aloudien Sedick, who would have faced a similar problem taking measurements to alter my trousers.

I am still afraid of crowds. I imagine that masses of people exhaling all kinds of germs might suddenly rush at me with autograph books or endeavor to examine me at close quarters. My fears increased when I was approached even in the loneliest places. One day Eileen and I drove by taxi to the Table Bay harbor. The driver

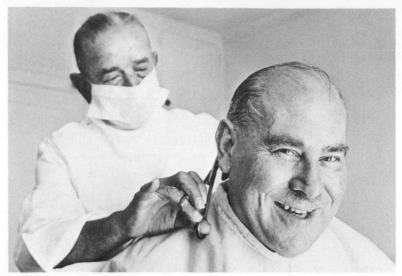

Dr. Blaiberg's first haircut after
discharge. Barney Albert, the barber, comes
to the apartment to do the job.

Wearing a tie for the first time
after twelve months.

parked at an isolated spot, and we sat back comfortably to watch the gulls swoop low over the water, listen to the gentle wash of the waves against the quayside and see the coming and going of ships.

Suddenly two schoolchildren, aged about nine or ten, thrust an autograph book through the open window. "Please sign this for us, Dr. Blaiberg," they said. They did not inquire whether I was, in fact, Dr. Blaiberg. It was a new experience for me, but one to which I was soon to be accustomed.

I love children and did not want to disappoint them. I signed my name, as instructed, then reluctantly rolled up the windows and set off for home. I was taking no chances.

On a subsequent drive to the Muizenberg beach, mainly deserted at that time of the year, a lone bather watched me clamber out of a car and said, "Congratulations. You deserve all the happiness you can get. I think you are a brave man." Then, tucking a surfboard under his arm, he walked off. "You're welcome to borrow my board any time you like, Doc."

I laughed. "Maybe I'll take up that offer one day."

As I walked along the soft, white sands, I looked longingly at the waves rolling inshore. "This is where I'm going to have my first swim," I said to the friend accompanying me.

Another awkward encounter came about two weeks after the children had spotted me at the harbor. I was on a trip to Signal Hill, admiring the grandeur of sea and mountain, when the door of a nearby car slammed. I saw the glint of recognition in the motorist's eye as he approached with a cigarette box, obviously for use as an autograph book.

"Not too close, please," I said extending a warning

hand and turning away my face. At first he ignored my request. Perhaps he thought I was just shy or putting on an act. Then he realized he had to keep his distance. He passed the cigarette box to my companion who handed it to me, and I scrawled my name all over it.

Another day I was driven to the Rhodes Memorial, on the slopes of Devil's Peak which overlooks the sweep of Cape Town's southern suburbs. As I stood there two men walked down the steps toward me but kept their distance.

"Do you know you have become famous in Britain?" one of them remarked. He introduced himself as Kenneth Griffith, then visiting South Africa for preliminary work on a film of Cecil Rhodes' life. With him was Dr. Richard Heald, a young surgical registrar at Guy's Hospital, London, then attending the biennial conference of the Association of Surgeons at Groote Schuur Hospital. He had come to South Africa as a ship's surgeon. We sat apart on the low wall encircling the memorial and chatted about heart transplants.

"I discussed your operation with Lord Russell Brock *," he told me. "He has a great admiration for Professor Barnard and his achievements." We spoke about the drugs I was taking and the treatment I was still undergoing at hospital. I did not realize how critically, and professionally, he had observed me during our chat.

A month later he wrote to *The Times* of London: "There have been a number of wild and varied reports about the quality of life being enjoyed by Dr. Blaiberg since his heart transplant. I met him, and a brief description by an essentially unbiased observer, like myself, may be of interest.

"He walks and talks and lives normally with the excep-

* One of Britain's leading heart specialists and President of the Royal College of Surgeons.

tion of a slight residual weakness of the legs. At no time did I observe him to be breathless.

" 'I have had a hundred days of good life on borrowed time,' he said, 'and if I die next week from rejection, the operation on me will still have been a success.'

"Having seen for myself that Dr. Blaiberg is enjoying life, I can assure doubters that reports to the contrary are untrue."

I recall that Mr. Griffith was more concerned than I about the chilly weather that afternoon—it was after five o'clock and the sun had dipped behind the mountain. But I have never believed in mollycoddling myself. I found the cold invigorating, and believe it is good for one's body to be exposed briefly to temperature extremes.

I began to entertain more people at my apartment. Over the Passover, which coincided with the Easter weekend, I had nine visitors one day. Most were relatives. One asked, anxiously, whether it was "safe" for me. Wasn't I taking a chance?

"Safe?" I said. "I can't live in a sterilized cocoon for the rest of my life."

When I think of all that my operation meant, I call to mind the changed life of Dorothy Haupt. She was invited to address meetings, judge beauty competitions, appear at premieres. She flew to Brazil to appear on television, the only woman in the world at the time, to have given permission for her husband's heart to be used in a transplant. I was able to make her trip even more exciting by passing on an invitation, sent to me, to visit a famous Lisbon restaurant. She spent two days in Lisbon, and no guest at the restaurant was more royally entertained. In Brazil she was feted, cheered, taken on special sight-seeing tours.

Even our maid Katie has been in the publicity spotlight.

The recipe for her egg soufflé is now used in hotels and restaurants, and she had a marriage proposal from a Johannesburg man who saw her photograph in a newspaper. She turned it down. She has a suitor.

Eileen's life has changed most. Not long ago she was a quiet-living, little-known housewife with a dying husband. She worked hard as a clerk to earn much-needed cash. Most nights she sat with me trying to comfort and sustain me. Occasionally she played a game of bridge or bowls with women friends but without enjoyment; my worsening condition was always in her mind.

Suddenly, everything was changed as if by magic. Today she is one of the best-known and most sought-after women in Cape Town. She has become, though not of her own seeking, a celebrity. People point at her in the street with something like awe and say, "That's Eileen Blaiberg. Her husband is Dr. Blaiberg, the man with the new heart." At first she was embarrassed and blushed. Now she smiles instead.

Invitations arrive endlessly for her to attend film and stage premières, cocktail parties, lunches and dinners. She is in demand as guest of honor at meetings of charitable and other organizations and as a public speaker though she had never spoken in public before. She travels to country towns more than a hundred miles from Cape Town to lecture and help raise funds (with considerable success) for the Chris Barnard Fund and the Cardiac Clinic Fund to further cardiac research.

People planning to visit South Africa to see me ask her to arrange appointments. My diary grows full. Our two telephones rarely stop ringing. New York and London are often on the line. What, editors want to know, do Eileen and I think of this and that? Or the latest transplant? Will we write something for them?

Eileen entertains our daily procession of guests, many of wide renown in science, medicine, and the arts, from the United States, Britain, Germany, and France, with expert ease and a ready smile even when they perhaps unwittingly, tend to delay our meal-times and my pill routine. What a born hostess and diplomat Eileen is!

She has naturally become far more clothes-conscious and has had to restock her wardrobe and include, among other clothes, a long, formal frock she would have had little occasion to wear before. Soon she will have to order another.

She now has a large personal correspondence, to which she replies meticulously, besides helping me to sort and reply to the fifty or sixty letters which still arrive daily for me from all parts of the world. Moreover, she finds time to accompany me to the hospital for my periodical checks and has even written a fairy story. This is how it happened.

I had a request from the United Nations Children's Fund (UNICEF) to contribute a fairy tale to an international publication. As one of a number of "leading personalities," I was asked to write a story to bring joy to the world's children. The proceeds were for charity.

"Who? Me?" I said to Eileen. "I've told a lot of stories in my time. But a fairy story . . ."

"Then I'll write it," she said, "and it'll be about you."

It didn't take her long. She wrote about a man who was dying. He wondered how long he had to live. He gave up hope and began to despair. His heart was sick. Then along came a fairy godfather named Chris Barnard. And what do you think he gave the man? A new heart. He had a happy life once more and could look to the future with hope.

UNICEF was delighted. The story was published. I

wonder how Chris Barnard will enjoy being cast in the role of fairy godfather!

Film stars and theatrical artists are often among our visitors. Maybe a chat and a photograph of me with them offers a little useful publicity. I don't mind.

When Liberace was in Cape Town he called on me, and Eileen attended the theater where he gave a performance. He invited her to stand up so that the audience could give her a "big hand." He spoke a few words about her courage, and the comfort she was to me in my illness and announced that he had dedicated the song "The Impossible Dream" to her and to me. It was the first time, he said, an "Impossible Dream" had come true.

Not many months ago Eileen would have preferred to sink through the floor than face a huge audience with the spotlight on her. She sought no escape now. She took a bow and acknowledged the "big hand."

Is she weary of it? Finding it too much of a strain? Though I sometimes detect a stifled yawn, I feel she is still enjoying herself in her exciting new life and role in which she can also do so much for so many that was impossible before. And I, with husbandly pride, watch her as she sallies forth from our apartment, knowing she will be among the most attractive and smartest women at any function she attends. How much happier can a man be in his wife?

I could go on mentioning others whose lives have been changed by what has happened to me; the millions of heart sufferers to whom the success of my operation has brought new hope. There are those who appear to have a "thrill," as the newspapers call it, by speaking to me as I stand on my balcony. Sometimes there is a little pathos, too.

An elderly woman wept when she sat in our apartment,

but they were not tears of sadness. Her husband had died of a heart attack, and here was I, alive with a new heart. She sobbed in her happiness for me and for Eileen.

Others are continually offering me gifts or their services for nothing, like Barney, my barber, who came to cut my hair and refused payment. I sent a donation, instead, to the School Feeding Scheme which provides food for under-privileged children. It will feed a child for ninety days. The receipt went to Barney.

Was he proud! Even more so, as he had cut Professor Barnard's famous tousled hair a few months before. What more could a barber hope for?

Friday, April 5, 1968, was a very special day for Eileen and me. It was our thirty-second wedding anniversary. We celebrated with a quiet dinner party in our apartment—just Eileen, her brother, his wife, and me. We drank a champagne toast to our good fortune. How different from our thirty-first anniversary. I had been in the hospital then for a month after my serious heart attack, and the doctors told Eileen there was no hope for me. Who had heard of heart transplants a year ago? They belonged only to science fiction. She believed we would never celebrate another wedding anniversary. I sent her flowers to brighten her day. She shed tears over them.

This year it was different. Now there is promise of a full and healthy life for me, and our marriage has a future as well as a past. Eileen was as excited as a young newlywed on her first anniversary. We had gifts for each other and handed them over before the party. I had bought her a beautiful antelope coat—the nicest she had ever owned, she said—and she reciprocated with a smart dark gray overcoat for winter though, frankly, I would have been perfectly satisfied to have continued wearing my old raincoat. But you know women. She said she had

Photo by *The Cape Argus*

Dr. and Mrs. Blaiberg celebrating their thirty-second
wedding anniversary on April 5, 1968.

to "smarten" me up with everyone paying attention to what I do, where I go.

In addition to the gift of the antelope coat, I told her to have her diamond engagement ring reset. I was spoiling her, she said. How I loved spoiling her. She deserved it all and so much more besides.

Looking back over our thirty-two years together, I realize that our happiness has stemmed from a lesson learned early in our mariage—one partner must always be prepared to back down after an argument. When arguments and bickering go on and on, unhappiness begins. Sulking is as bad as it is unpleasant. Every couple has disagreements but they must be ended *and* forgotten as quickly as possible.

Don't let me give you the impression for one moment, that I am a perfect husband. Far from it. I have my faults and fads, but Eileen, with true feminine guile and intuition, has her own way of dealing with them and us.

She knows, for instance, that I am an independent sort of chap who feels quite confident and capable of looking after himself—even now. I hate being fussed over. So what does she do? Listen to what she told a reporter:

"People often ask me whether I have to give Phil a lot of attention to make sure he takes his pills regularly and dresses warmly when the weather turns chilly. The answer is that I do, but I dare not do it in such a way that he realizes it.

"For instance, I mustn't remind him when to take his pills. He is too independent for that. He keeps his own little record book.

"But I do keep a secret eye on him. He doesn't always know it, but I watch carefully to see that he doesn't do anything too strenuous or dangerous. I try my best not to let him know. He'd soon pick me out if he did."

She's darn right. I'd soon pick her out if ever I caught her watching me. But I don't and haven't.

At the risk of being considered by some as indelicate, I am adding a footnote to the account of our anniversary party.

I can speak from experience when I say that it is in your own interests and only fair to your doctors that you should withhold no information from them through modesty or any other reason. They can only assess and arrive at a diagnosis of your case when they have all the facts about you.

With this in mind I have always told my physician everything and never more so than now when my medical history is being compiled for official records and textbooks on cardiology and cardiac surgery. Consequently, I mentioned that my wife and I had resumed our marital relations twenty days after my departure from the hospital—on our wedding anniversary. He regarded the information as important and suggested I tell others as well to allay the fears of some men who believe their potency might be impaired after cardiac surgery.

As the weeks passed, I looked well and felt even better. My legs were becoming stronger, and I enjoyed my brief strolls. I had a good tan from basking in the warm autumn sunshine on the veranda of our apartment. I loved the car drives that took me regularly to the seaside and into the country where I could breathe the good air and feel the crackle of the leaves under my feet as I roamed through the forests.

It was time for a tolerance checkup, in which, for more than an hour, the doctors tested the reaction of my body to exercise. They placed me on a machine like a bicycle without wheels, and I was required to pedal for six minutes. The resistance of the pedals was increased in stages and, with each, the reaction of my heart noted. I had to breathe into bags to provide samples of my breath for analysis; the doctors were well satisfied with the results.

One of the young nurses said, maybe flatteringly, that she would not have been able to pedal as well as I. Whether this was so or not, I felt the exercise had benefited me. I experienced no strain, and I could not feel my heart beating as most people do when they exert themselves.

The only strain was in my legs, particularly in the thighs which still need building up. My legs are not yet as powerful and stocky as they were, but I am sure they will be one day.

I enjoyed this visit to the hospital as I had the opportunity of meeting the doctors from Australia and Spain. They, too, examined me. I have no objection to tests, or examination, or cross-examination as a "unique" human being. There is always the possibility that some scientific benefit might come of this.

Now, for a change, let us talk about food. Everyone does these days. One is too fat, another too thin. And appropriate diets are earnestly discussed and calories counted as though they are mystic symbols in some be-your-correct-weight ritual.

For myself, I believe in the adage: "Don't live to eat. Rather eat to live."

By planning your diet carefully you can live a healthier and more comfortable life. But don't get into the hands of the food faddists. You would be surprised how many people have asked me the dietary requirements for one with a transplanted heart as though this would make him unique in his eating habits.

I can eat anything I fancy. The doctors have warned

me only against salt. I must not take salty foods because salt retains fluids, and this is bad for me. For the rest it is *carte blanche*. But I adopt the commonsense approach and apply my own restrictions.

I still have to watch my weight carefully and keep a wary eye on a paunch that once gave me the appearance of being a heavy beer drinker, which I am not. Before I entered the hospital my weight was up to 175 pounds. During my illness it dropped by more than twenty pounds. Now, as I write, it is 160 pounds. I don't want it higher.

I have to confess that I rather indulged myself when I came home, and Katie encouraged me. I had huge breakfasts with hearty helpings of chops and eggs. Those are now taboo. Instead, breakfast is a light meal, generally a bowl of cereal, a cup of skimmed milk, and cheese. With an eye on the waistline I have stopped eating toast. All our household milk is skimmed so that's what our visitors get in their tea or coffee. I drink neither.

By lunch time I have developed a good appetite, and Eileen and I generally have a meat course with vegetables and sweets, fruit—fresh or canned—with ice cream. This is washed down with a plentiful supply of water, which I have always enjoyed with my meals. Supper is of fish, steamed or fried. Occasionally I have boiled potatoes, though I try to cut down on starches as much as possible.

I am allowed as much sugar as I like, but I avoid sweet dishes, again because of that waistline which is as important to me as it is to the most fastidious, weight-conscious woman. So, all in all, I keep to a normal diet. The restrictions, save for salt, are self-imposed. I am permitted one egg a day, but I confine myself to two a week.

My beer drinking has provided the newspapers with lots of copy and headlines but with varying degrees of accuracy or inaccuracy. I enjoy the occasional pint. What

South African, Englishman, American or Australian, or any other kind of chap, doesn't?

However, I don't drink a lot because my fluid intake is limited to three thousand cc's a day. A small twelve-ounce bottle of beer contains about 360 cc's of fluid. So two beers a day account for 720 cc's of my quota. I make up the rest with water and milk.

Apart from observing my diet, which has benefited me greatly, I take my temperature twice a day and faithfully carry out my exercises. I don't overdo them, only ten minutes at a time. They are not strenuous but effective and help to build up my still weakened legs and stomach muscles. And I continue my breathing execises which still form part of the old recovery campaign.

In the afternoons I have a nap for an hour and a half, and the rest of my time is devoted to reading and catching up with, or trying to keep abreast of, correspondence from all parts of the world.

Preparation of this book has also kept me occupied. The only trouble I encountered was the inability to read some of my notes. My handwriting, I must admit, is atrocious.

As a youth I once started an adventure yarn but, after filling five pages of an exercise book, I could not decipher the most thrilling passages and gave up in despair. Now, however, that I believe I have an interesting, even exciting, true-to-life tale to tell, I keep at it and have often been surprised at my continued application.

After I had been at home a month, I felt it was time to assess my progress. I could scarcely believe that it was just four weeks since I took those first, groggy steps into the sunlight and fresh air outside the hospital. It seemed more like a year.

I had learned to walk almost normally. True, I still

needed a helping hand up or down the stairs, but that was a minor worry. Then the doctors had reduced the dosage of pills, which was another source of comfort—the problem was to establish a "base line" on which to work. With other operations or diseases, they merely look up previous data obtained from other patients and prescribe accordingly. In my case, however, they had no such figures, only a little data to work on following the operation on Louis Washkansky.

I realize I will have to take pills regularly for the rest of my life, as many other people do, but my dosage will be reduced until the desirable level has been reached.

My diary shows that I was gradually tackling new tasks. I am a determined sort of person, but, as a medical man, I know that overdoing things can be just as dangerous as not doing anything. For example, during the first week after I left the hospital, I did not attempt to get into the bathtub. During the next I stepped in with Eileen's assistance, taking care I did not slip and injure myself. At the end of the month, I could get in myself with comparative ease, though getting out again was still a little awkward.

A big event in my postoperative life came about six weeks after I returned home. I drove my car for the first time in many months. How I had been looking forward to that day. And how Eileen had been dreading it. But I had made up my mind, and nothing would make me change it. Friends had taken my car from the garage from time to time to warm up the engine so that I would have no difficulty in starting. The day before, I drove the car into my garage to prove to myself I was not tackling too much. I need not have worried.

I timed my adventure for five o'clock the following afternoon. Eileen was agitated. "Don't you realize it's the rush hour? Everyone will be returning home from work then. And you *know* Cape Town drivers—always in a hurry! Make it some other time when there's less traffic on the road."

"I'm going," I said, "rush hour or not." Eileen had intended accompanying me, but she had letters to mail. In any event, I thought, if she came along, she might qualify as the next heart transplant patient. So I invited a friend of mine, an experienced driver, to be my passenger.

Our neighbors looked anxiously from their balconies overlooking the row of garages when I opened the door of my car and climbed behind the steering wheel. I switched on the engine and prepared to back out. But I found unexpected difficulty in reversing. The gear lever had to be lifted and then pushed into reverse. My arm muscles were a little too stiff.

Motorists take for granted the simple act of reversing their cars a dozen times a day. A flick of the lever and it's done. But when you have been bedridden and unable to use your arm muscles for a time, they become stiff. You have difficulty in using them.

Anyhow, I soon overcame that. In a moment or two I had reversed, revved up the engine, and invited my passenger to hop in, assuring him he was in no peril of his life.

I edged out of the apartment block grounds into the busy main road. To the left was an intersection controlled by traffic lights. Peak hour traffic was, as Eileen had said, piling up rapidly. Cars followed one another, inches apart, with the occasional driver hooting impatiently and gesticulating as though he feared arrival at his liquor store after closing hour.

Ahead of us was a side street with only an occasional car alongside the pavement. "Drive along there," my companion said, "and you'll avoid the traffic."

"I don't want to avoid the traffic," I told him. "I want

practice *in* traffic, plenty of it." I swung into a long procession.

We had traveled barely a mile when I felt my confidence as a driver returning. Perhaps, I swerved slightly more than I needed to avoid parked cars, and I didn't change gears at exactly the right moment, but these faults were soon corrected. I did, however, require a little more concentration than I anticipated.

We traveled about five miles, weaving in and out of the traffic, occasionally bothered by illegally parked cars. Then I stopped. My friend believed I had had enough.

"Would you like me to drive you back, Phil?" he asked. "After all, this is only your first outing."

"Not jolly likely," I thanked him. "I'm really enjoying myself now. I feel I 'belong' again even if there are some rotten drivers on the road. I want a lot more practice. What a surprise I'd give Jill if I could drive my car to the airport to meet her when she arrives from Israel."

The return journey I found easier. I told myself, however, that I should guard against overconfidence, take no chances. Soon I was gliding into my garage. One of my neighbors, who had watched the start of my drive and expected the worst, was obviously relieved to see me and the car in one piece.

"I was so worried about you," she said. "You know what Cape Town drivers are like."

"Yes," I said. "But I've just had one of the most wonderful experiences of my life." Eileen, who had been on pins and needles, was glad to see me back, too. I thought the occasion called for a beer. I enjoyed it as much as the drive.

After that I took the wheel when I drove to hospital for my regular checkups. Once, after I had pulled away from a parking lot, I saw someone swinging along the road in a hurry.

I stopped and called out the offer of a lift. "Going my way?" he asked.

"Any way you say," I replied. I looked at the tousled hair and the wide grin. You've guessed right. It was Chris Barnard.

It was the day after I had driven my car that I had a visit from Liberace, the world's most flamboyant, or flamboyantly-dressed entertainer. An appointment had been arranged for 3:30 p.m., but we had a call explaining that his chauffeur had lost his way in the suburban by-paths. He was confident, however, of tracking us down.

Eventually he arrived at about four o'clock with his manager, Seymour Heller, his manager's wife, Billie, and John Clarke, local director of a chain of theaters. He was dressed in a doublebreasted suit with blue cravat-type tie and wore, of course, his famous rings, one with a diamond-studded piano.

I had spruced up, too, with flannels, Royal Dental College blazer, and cravat. But when I saw Liberace . . .

"They say we are both world celebrities," I greeted him. "Your fame has been self-made. Mine has been thrust on me. But I'm sure of one thing. You must be the world's best-dressed celebrity, and I'm certainly the shabbiest."

Liberace laughed heartily. "Oh, no, not at all," he said. "You look simply marvelous, so well. What do clothes matter?" I knew they mattered a lot to him.

We sat in the lounge. The first item on the program was, inevitably, taking photographs. Mrs. Heller had a polaroid flash camera and, within minutes, we were examining the results.

Liberace opened the conversation dramatically. "Dr. Blaiberg, do you know that I also cheated death? And I was also saved by the tragic death of another man."

It was November 22, 1963.

Photo by *The Cape Argus*

Dr. Blaiberg feels fit enough to take a walk along the beach.

Photo by Don Mackenzie

Dr. Barnard's most famous patient
takes the doctor for a ride.

Photo by *The Cape Argus*

Mail came in from all over the world.

"I had acute kidney failure caused by the inhalation of carbon tetrachloride, a cleaning fluid," he told me. "My costumes had been cleaned with it and hung in the room where I slept. I was unaware that I was breathing in poisonous fumes which were slowly causing my death.

"It was just at that time that President John Kennedy was assassinated in Dallas, Texas. My manager burst into my room to waken me and tell me the news. If he hadn't, well, he would have found a dead man in the morning.

"But I was desperately ill. I was taken to the hospital by ambulance, and a priest administered the last rites. Treatment was unsuccessful at first but then I responded and recovered after five weeks without any aftereffects.

"So," he added, "we are both here today by a million-to-one chance."

After we had chatted a while I decided to have some of my own back. I had signed thousands of autograph books. Now I wanted someone else's signature—his. He drew a piano and with a flourish added "Liberace."

A week later another world-famous American entertainer, Shelley Berman, rang the door bell. Gags come thick and fast when Shelley is around. He told me he had "demanded" to see me.

"Even if I don't see Professor Barnard," he said, "at least I'll have seen a product of his labor. It must have been hard labor, but he certainly made a good job of it."

Katie produced tea and chocolate cake. As Eileen served she moved between us and apologized.

"I don't mind if a woman comes between me and a man," Shelley quipped. "But I do mind if a man comes between me and a woman."

I must have talked quite a lot that day because Shelley said afterward, "The only bad audience I met in South Africa was Philip Blaiberg. He won't listen. He has had a mouth transplant." But when he did get in a word or two in the Blaiberg apartment he said, "At least this transplant has given some of my countrymen an education. They now know this is a civilized country. When I went to be fitted for a suit for South Africa, I had to convince my tailor that it was not necessary for me to wear a pith helmet here. 'Maniac,' I said, 'I'm not gonna be Tarzan down there.'

"But I must say this. Johannesburg is one of the few cities in the world where you can wake up and hear the birds coughing."

In more serious vein, Shelley said Professor Barnard had ended South Africa's isolation in the world though there still were some who thought the country "just a direction." He would have liked to perform in more South African cities and Rhodesia and even in Zambia though there was the risk there that President Kaunda might "nationalize" him as he had certain other business enterprises.

Fame has its advantages as well as its penalties. I would much rather have remained plain Philip Blaiberg, unknown to the world, than have climbed to the top rung of the ladder by the steps I did. But now that fame has, so to say, been forced upon me. I would be less than human if I did not enjoy some of the excitement, the pleasures and surprises that come to celebrities.

On the human, personal side I have made innumerable friends all over the globe through newspapers and television, and their good wishes and inquiries after my health and progress I shall treasure always. Even my indifferent singing in my bath, relayed over one TV program has, apparently, done nothing yet to damage my own, or South Africa's, image abroad.

On the material side Eileen and I have been showered with gifts of every kind. Beautiful bouquets arrive at our apartment almost daily; nothing delights Eileen more than flowers.

I have been invited to appear on television in Brazil and other lands. The Czechoslovak Socialist Party, in Vastin CSSR, wants me as a postoperational guest at the famous Podebrady spa where heart disease cases are treated. I have been asked to take the waters at spas in West Germany.

Airlines have offered Eileen and me free flights to any country we choose, with luxury hotel accommodation. Leading restaurants in Europe want to entertain us and serve us their exotic dishes prepared by famous chefs. But though I am as well as I can expect, travel abroad is not yet for me. I hope, however, to take advantage of some of these generous offers in the days to come. At the moment I regard them as pleasures deferred.

The International Academy of Orthodontics of Lakewood, California has made me an honorary member, and others in my profession in Taipei, Taiwan, Formosa, and Japan hope to welcome me to the Orient. The Rotary Club of Mangague, Colombia, South America, has inquired whether I am a coffee drinker. They plan to send me supplies from their country, "reputed [they claim] to be the best in the world."

I have been offered "miracle" cures for various bodily ailments, from which, happily, I do not suffer. Songs have been written about me and poems composed for me. My autographed photographs are said to be in greater demand than those of many film stars.

My daily postbag has, for months, been a fascinating surprise packet. I have been deluged by thousands of letters from every land outside Red China. Most are from the United States. They are delivered whether correctly addressed or mailed merely to "Dr. Blaiberg (transplant) South Africa."

They come from men, women, and children of all ages, from business and professional men, professors, doctors, teachers and students, from cranks, autograph hunters, advice givers and seekers. I am told of family problems, cases of ill-health and tragedy that would fill a book on their own.

It takes me hours to reply to them all, mostly in brief autographed acknowledgment, others more fully when I am asked for comment of a personal nature or encouragement for good causes. At first philatelists regarded me as an answer to their dreams. I gave them stamps rarely seen in South Africa with lavish abandon. Now they are sent to the Israeli wounded of the Six-Day-War for occupational therapy purposes.

You will agree, I think, that I did not exaggerate when I said that life at home, with a new heart and a new outlook, has been marvelous. Only one thing has upset me during these days of excitement, challenge, and the great adventure of living again—the unwarranted criticism directed at Professor Barnard and his heart transplant team.

The arch critic has been Dr. William Dempster, a surgeon of Hammersmith Hospital, London, England. He and several other cardiologists said heart transplant operations were premature and they doubted I would recover. It was obvious, from television screenings, according to Dr. Dempster, that I was still breathless.

When Dr. M. C. Botha, the team's immunologist was asked, "Are heart transplant operations premature?" his reply was that the question should be put to me.

It was. This is my reply:

The suggestion of breathlessness is nonsense. The television picture, to which Dr. Dempster referred, was taken long before I was discharged from hospital. At that time, I walked round the two rooms of the transplant unit ten times on five occasions daily without showing any signs of breathlessness. After all, I should know better than one who bases his judgment on a picture taken months ago.

I would challenge Dr. Dempster to walk up and down my balcony and carry out my leg exercises which are pretty strenuous. Then let us see how breathless he is. I will willingly compare his breathlessness with mine.

Was the operation premature? I should say not. I have never felt better in years.

Let me quote, for Dr. Dempster's benefit, from a recent address by Professor J. F. Brock, President of the South African College of Physicians, Surgeons, and Gynaecologists, to a special convocation of the College in Cape Town:

"Academic knowledge and scientific progress are more advanced in many parts of the world, but Professor Chris Barnard has been able to lead his team into a breakthrough. . . .

"It is a feat of teamwork in the craftmanship of professional competence. The problems it has raised are as much problems of professional ethics and propriety as they are academic and scientific problems. . . ."

Do not, Dr. Dempster, begrudge me my time, even borrowed time, and the opportunity to enjoy the rest of my days by doubting my recovery. Instead, I suggest you, too, salute Professor Barnard and his gallant, dedicated team, for their courage in undertaking an unprecedented operation. His and their achievements will surely benefit mankind in the years to come.

If your dismal prophecy about me proves correct, you will be able to say, "I told you so." If not, let your statement fade into oblivion.

Let me extend you an invitation to visit Cape Town. I

176

will meet you at the airport and drive you to my apartment in my car. We will sit in my lounge, perhaps have a drink, and you can assess the degree of my recovery. You will realize how wonderful I find it to be well and alive after being so near to death.

I have come to the end of my story, a story in which destiny has played a role on the chessboard of my life with me as its pawn. There are a number of thoughts that have helped me to overcome many crises in my own life. Should more arise in future, I believe they will do so again and sustain me.

Life is sweet for some, bitter for others, brief for all of us. We are, as Shakespeare says, mere players on a vast stage.

> Out, out, brief candle!
> Life's but a walking shadow, a poor player
> That struts and frets his hour upon the stage
> And then is heard no more. It is a tale
> Told by an idiot, full of sound and fury,
> Signifying nothing.

Let us remember that, make the most of that brief hour. To those correspondents who have asked me for my formula for a happy life, my reply has been: "Do what you like—and like what you do! If you are a square peg in a round hole, get out of the round hole into a square hole as soon as you can. It's later than you think."

I have avoided loan and debt as my mother taught me. I never argue with a tradesman as I believe a workman is worthy of his hire. It is a rule which, I sometimes wished, was practiced by some of my patients. How I would have liked to enclose those immortal lines from

Hamlet with my unpaid accounts when they were mailed each month.

> Neither a borrower, nor a lender be;
> For a loan oft loses both itself and friend,
> And borrowing dulls the edge of husbandry.
> This above all: to thine own self be true,
> And it must follow, as the night the day,
> Thou canst not then be false to any man.

In my confirmed belief in fatalism and the futility of trying to reverse, or alter, what has been done, or influencing what fate has ordained for us in the future, I turn to the words of Omar Khayyam which have been the guiding principle of my life:

> The Moving Finger writes; and, having writ,
> Moves on: nor all your Piety nor Wit
> Shall lure it back ot cancel half a Line,
> Nor all your Tears wash out a Word of it.

So what use are tears? Live for the day. Do not regret or torture yourself with the might-have-beens.

Up till now, in spite of trials and tribulations, I consider myself singularly fortunate. It frightens me at times because, as in a Greek tragedy, I think that when my luck changes, as it might, tragedy will strike in the end.

Meanwhile, whatever days, months or years remain to me, I shall take them as they come and make the most of them as happily as I can.

EPILOGUE:

BACK FROM THE BRINK

BY BENJAMIN BENNETT

D r. Blaiberg and I had arranged to scan the final draft of the manuscript on the night of May 23, 1968. He was due to return to Groote Schuur Hospital next day, his fifty-ninth birthday, for a thorough examination and checkup.

I found him sitting on a bed in pajamas and dressing gown. He apologized wryly for receiving me in his bedroom.

"I feel so terribly tired," he said. "All done in."

I ragged him. "Phil," I said, "you shouldn't have coached the Lions and shown them how to pass and catch a rugby ball. You probably overtaxed yourself in the process."

He smiled. "No, it isn't that. I've got a general feeling of weariness in all my limbs. Tell me," he asked, "how do I look to you since you met me two months ago?"

Truthfully, I said he appeared to me to be much better though I had noticed some lassitude or fatigue in him for several days. But a short while resting in the hospital, protected from too many interviewers and visitors, would no doubt help to put him right.

When the hospital tests were over he went home, pending arrival from Germany of special equipment to take a moving picture of the transplanted heart. This careful and scientific assessment of his condition would not only help the doctors supervise his progress but also provide information that would prove valuable in achieving success in future transplants.

Soon after his re-admission he became seriously ill. The doctors diagnosed hepatitis, a disease of the liver. There are various types of this, depending on whether the liver is attacked by bacteria, a virus, or the toxic effects of drugs.

At first, members of the transplant team were unable to decide which type of the disease was present. As, however, the commonest form is caused by an infecting virus, he was moved to the sterilized suite he had originally occupied where he was protected against the entry of germs. But the possibility that the illness might be a sign of rejection of the heart could not, at first, be ruled out.

Soon fear was expressed for his life. At times he was barely conscious; in his waking moments, too tired even to speak to his wife and daughter separated from him by the protective glass partition. Nevertheless, he fought against the illness that had stricken him with the same indomitable courage he had shown before and after the operation.

His spirit burned steadily, feeble though his body had become. His will and determination to live remained unquenchable. This assisted the doctors. Yet they faced an agonizing dilemma in a situation where no precedent existed to guide them.

The immuno-suppressive drugs he had been taking for five months appeared to have effectively prevented rejection of the heart. But they had, at the same time, suppressed the immunological system—the system that empowers the body to overcome invading germs.

The processes that lead to the rejection of transplanted organs are the same as those that reject—that is, destroy or neutralize—bacteria and viruses. If the suppressive drugs were stopped to permit the patient's immunological system to combat the germs, rejection of the heart was sure to follow. Yet, unless this defence system were allowed to act, he might succumb to the infection.

If bacteria, as opposed to a virus, were causing the infection, the antirejection drugs could be continued as treatment with antibiotics would overcome the infection even though the patient's protective mechanisms were prevented from acting.

If, however, the infection were due to a virus, the outlook was grim. Antibiotics are ineffective against viruses, and only the patient's own immunological mechanisms would enable him to overcome a viral infection. But these mechanisms, if allowed freedom to act, would reject the heart.

For days the doctors were in a quandary, confronted with grave alternatives while their patient's life trembled in the balance. Once more the name of Blaiberg captured the headlines and television news bulletins. Top newspaper correspondents flew into Cape Town from London, New York, Paris, and Australia to keep a 24-hour-a-day "death watch" and provide full coverage. Mrs. Blaiberg's two telephones and the Groote Schuur switchboard were swamped with overseas calls. Cables and letters of sympathy and goodwill arrived again in shoals.

The *Cape Argus* editorialized:

"Dr. Philip Blaiberg has an assured place in history. The way in which he challenged life itself—and went home triumphantly with the heart of another beating strongly within him—gave modern medicine a new dimension.

"Yet it is more than that, more than medical history. Brought back from the brink by a miracle of surgery and specialist aftercare, his jovial but pragmatic approach to

183

life has been an inspiration to all. By his courage he has strengthened others.

"Dr. Blaiberg was recently asked how he felt about the future. He replied: 'I used to worry a tremendous amount, but I no longer have that attitude toward life. Some years ago I read a book which gave the advice that one should not try to go back to the past, for that is forgotten, nor can you live in the future. The answer is to live each day *only* for that day. That seemed reasonable to me. And *that* is my philosophy now.'

"All South Africa and, indeed, the world will wish Philip Blaiberg a full recovery from his present serious setback."

It was finally established that the infection was caused, not by a virus, but by bacteria. There was, therefore, no need to stop the antirejection drugs. Antibiotics controlled the infection and the patient began to improve slowly.

Still, the time of anxiety was by no means over for Mrs. Blaiberg, Jill, or the transplant team. The public did not know, and could not guess, the almost unendurable strain and tension and sleepless nights that lay behind the terse hospital bulletins recording "No change" or "Slight improvement."

"I don't think that in all the months of Phil's illness, going back to March, 1967, had I experienced a more nerve-racking time," Eileen Blaiberg told me.

"It started on May 24 when he went for his checkup. The doctors had given me to understand that their examination would be merely routine though they did mention they were slightly worried about his fatigue during the previous few days.

"He was allowed to come home the following weekend for several days and then, on June 2, I was asked to take him back to the hospital. For the first few days all seemed to be going well. Then, one morning, when I arrived to visit him in the intensive care ward, I was told he had been moved to the sterile suite where he had been after the operation.

"Instinctively, I knew something was wrong. The doctors told me Phil was desperately ill with meningitis and hepatitis and they feared he might not make it. How I lived through the next few dreadful days is still a marvel to me. I was in a continual daze, my head was a blob of pain, and I dragged myself about like an automaton.

"Then, gradually, Phil began to recover. I cannot describe the relief and thankfulness and the new feeling of hope that were aroused in me. But hope was soon to be dashed again. After two days the doctors said Phil had developed circulatory trouble, and they advised me to standby in case the end came. So there I was, once more, in a state of hopelessness and despair.

"I visited Phil regularly twice a day but it brought little comfort to me. I saw him sinking before my eyes. He was pitifully thin and weak and could only manage a few words at a time to me. He begged me not to visit him while he was in this state. I was wasting my time, he said, talking to a stone. He confided to the nursing sisters the reason he did not want me there—he could not bear to see the suffering in my eyes. That was all he could see of me in my sterile outfit.

"In spite of what he said, I continued my usual visits. I told him I came out of selfish reasons. I wanted to see him for myself. After three days of agony I was greeted by the doctors with smiles. Phil's circulation was back to normal. Now, I bluffed myself, nothing could go wrong. Even I, as a layman, saw the jaundice was gradually lessening. The doctors confirmed it. . . ."

The daily bulletins ceased. Dr. Blaiberg was out of danger, the public was told, and regular bulletins on his condition were no longer warranted. But he remained in the suite, the world's longest lived heart transplant patient.

Then fate dealt a shattering blow. Dr. Blaiberg contracted pneumonia in what was thought to be virtually a germ-free ward. Thorough as the bacteriologists and doctors had been in creating a sterile world for him to recuperate in, a 100-to-one ill chance had occurred.

Once more he fought for his life. It was an unequal battle, one he had to wage without the vital weapon of bodily resistance. He could draw now only on his spirit and willpower, all but entirely sapped in a valiant struggle with hepatitis.

Let Mrs. Blaiberg take up the story:

"It was on Thursday, July 4, that the doctors told me Phil was desperately ill again, this time with pneumonia, and his chance of survival was slight. The news hit me like a sledgehammer. I spoke to him through the intercom. It was heartrending to look at him. To me he seemed even worse than just before the operation. Nothing, it appeared, could save him.

"One of the doctors tried to cheer me up. 'While there's life,' he said, 'there's hope.' But I felt the end was at hand. Phil was not made of iron. How much more could he fight and give of himself in the battle against his latest illness?

"I did not let Phil sense my fears and misgivings. I spoke as reassuringly as I could to him. I said I was certain he would get better.

" 'It's no use bluffing ourselves,' " he said. Each word was an effort. 'This time I want to go quietly.'

"I ignored the remark and spoke of the publication of

186

the book in which he had always taken such a lively interest. He smiled slightly and said in a barely audible whisper: 'I won't be here to see it.'

"On Saturday night, July 6, Professor Barnard said to me: 'Mrs. Blaiberg, if you don't want to lose your husband, we will have to consider giving him another heart transplant and also a lung.'

"I was stunned and unable to speak for some moments.

" 'Professor,' I asked, 'are you serious?'

" 'I've never been more so,' he said. 'And first of all I want your permission, if your husband is agreeable, to make a new transplant.'

"A feeling of clutching at a straw came over me. I said, 'Professor, if that is our only chance, we must take it.'

"It was decided not to tell Phil about the imminent possibility of a transplant until a donor had been found. But that night the team was alerted to stand by for an emergency operation.

"Professor Barnard had discussed with Phil, earlier, the prospect of a second, or even a third, transplant if his body rejected the donor hearts. He had not yet fully recovered from the hepatitis and still suffered lung complications. To undergo another operation in that condition would have entailed a greater risk than before.

"However, Phil did not hesitate. He was prepared to entrust his life entirely to the man who had saved it in the first instance. 'If it has to be done,' he said, 'it must be done.' "

Mrs. Blaiberg left Groote Schuur with a feeling of helplessness and hopelessness. She was utterly weary, close to exhaustion, her nerves worn thin and ragged.

The reports leaked in some mysterious way to the

press at this time were confusing and increased her anxieties. Only a handful of people knew all the facts, which could not be revealed just then. So newspapers speculated about a second heart transplant, put two and two together, and sometimes found the answer added up to an imminent, or completed, operation with the patient the first man in the world to have a third heart beating in his breast.

What a story! The mass circulation newspapers in Britain used it as their Page One lead; but the *Daily Mirror* protested against the spate of publicity.

"Everyone," it said, "would like to cheer this courageous transplant survivor back to health. But no one can have an easy mind over the wave of publicity about his condition every time he has a relapse.

"Heart transplant operations themselves are still highly controversial. They are made more controversial when they are associated, as in this particular case, with a constant bombardment of publicity, rumor and speculation.

"There have been stories that Dr. Blaiberg might be given a new heart and lungs. There have been reports that he refused a second transplant, reports denied by his wife and Professor Barnard.

"The whole business is enough to make any heart patient think twice before going through the same ordeal.

"Professor Barnard and Cape Town's Groote Schuur Hospital will always be under pressure to give out news, and they may not find it easy to achieve the right balance between candor and silence. But while the controversy about heart transplants continues, they should beware of the wrong kind of publicity and the harm it can do."

Mrs. Blaiberg agreed fully with these views. She was sickened, she said, by the way her words were misconstrued, distorted, and sensationalized, weary of the ceaseless pursuit by journalists, with a deadline to meet, who *had* to produce a story, *any* story each and every day, angry with others who invaded her privacy, telephoned at unearthly hours, and gave her no peace or rest.

And yet she could expect no less in these days of fierce, cut-throat competition between press, television, and radio. Her husband was again the world's most-talked-of celebrity and she had to shoulder the trials and burdens this cast upon her.

"By Sunday, July 7," Mrs. Blaiberg says, "the team had not yet found a donor and at 6:30 p.m., Dr. S. C. W. Bosman, in charge of Phil's postoperative care, said quietly to me: 'Eileen, you had better go into Phil's suite and speak to him.' Though he did not say it, I knew only too well what he meant by allowing me into a place that had always been out of bounds to me. It was to be my opportunity to say good-by.

"I was not told, at that stage, that the team had decided to use antilymphocyte serum (A L S) on Phil the previous day. The serum, developed after research in all parts of the world, is a means of striking the delicate balance necessary between suppression of rejection and retention of the body's ability to fight off rejection. Perhaps the doctors were doubtful whether it would prove effective and did not want to buoy me up with false hopes.

"I put on my sterile outfit, as usual, and walked into Phil's ward in fear and trepidation. My legs felt weak. I think I was near to fainting. He was dozing when I stood beside his bed and spoke to him. 'Phil. . . . PHIL. . . .'

"He opened his eyes and smiled faintly. 'Phil,' I said trying my best to sound pleased, 'look at the privilege they have given me to visit you right at your bedside.'

189

He shook his head slightly. His lips moved as though he were saying, 'You know as well as I do. This is the end of the road.'

"I had not planned, or thought, what exactly I would say. Then, suddenly, I heard myself pleading with him, 'Phil, you *have* to live. You've just *got* to live. Jill and I need you desperately.'

"I saw tears rolling down his face. I kept control of myslf. How, I don't know. Then I left him, as I thought, for the last time. It seemed unreal that I might never again hear him speak or see him smile, that all his fond hopes, and mine, might end within a matter of hours.

"When I returned to our apartment, I allowed myself the relief of tears for the first time in weeks. Once I started sobbing, I couldn't stop. All the anguish and suffering, the fears and dashed hopes of the past weeks and months, were in those bitter tears.

"Suddenly the telephone rang. So *IT* had happened already, I told myself. I had been just in time to say good-by. I was trembling like a leaf when I lifted the receiver. Professor Barnard was at the other end. I recognized his voice.

"I couldn't speak. My tongue was dry and stuck to the roof of my mouth. I wondered, vaguely, how he would break the news to me and tell of our great loss. For it would be his loss, too. I heard no sad or mournful voice but a happy one, excited, bubbling over.

"Mrs. Blaiberg," he said, "I've got *wonderful* news for you." He spoke the word 'wonderful' with fervor. "Your husband is going to live. He's going to live."

"For a moment I could hardly grasp the meaning of his words. 'Does that mean,' I asked, 'that you have found a donor?' "

" 'No,' he said excitedly. 'We don't need a transplant any longer. Your husband has rallied.'

"In my dazed state, I forgot to ask why the transplant was no longer necessary. I couldn't believe that a miracle had taken place, in some other way, to spare Phil. My brother took me and Jill to hospital. There, we heard, for the first time, that Phil had been given antilymphocyte serum on Saturday morning, July 6, and it had taken 36 hours to show its effects.

"From that time onward he seemed to improve slowly but surely. The day after I said good-by to him, he called for his breakfast. Instead of the milk he had sipped during previous days, he wanted steak and eggs. The following morning his appetite was even better. He ordered a breakfast of porridge, three eggs, cream cheese, and two glasses of milk. His circulation, I was told, had improved and his morale, as I could see, was excellent.

"To Dr. Bosman, who had tended him during most of the crisis period, he said with his old broad smile: 'Bossie, you and I are going on that overseas trip together after all.' "

Treatment with antilymphocyte serum continued with results so satisfactory that bulletins were again issued only periodically, and all recorded steady progress.

Dr. Blaiberg was examined by Dr. Denton Cooley, an eminent heart surgeon from Houston, Texas, who attended the first international heart transplant symposium in Cape Town in July, 1968. At that time he had three surviving heart transplant patients in the hospital, one due to resume full-time employment within a few weeks.

He found Dr. Blaiberg's heart a bit rapid, and he was a little short of breath but his lungs were clear. He was chatty and chirpy and, in Dr. Cooley's opinion, had every chance of recovering.

A few days later a bulletin announced that Dr. Blaiberg's lung complications had disappeared entirely and the hepatitis had virtually cleared up as well. Photographs showed him happy and smiling, giving his V for Victory sign. He had, indeed, gained a victory—for medical science—as great as any on the field of battle.

His wife and daughter, Jill, remain ever thankful for the miracle that spared him.

"How can I ever put into words," Eileen Blaiberg says, "my gratitude to Professor Barnard and his team of dedicated men for all they went through, for all they suffered for Phil; and especially Dr. Bosman who spent sleepless nights with him throughout his illness. It is devotion and unselfishness like this, that gives one faith in one's fellow men."

For myself, I will always cherish my friendship with one the world has saluted for his matchless courage and fortitude in bearing suffering with a smile.